D0098355

$5.00

THE CENTURY EARTH SCIENCE SERIES

Kirtley F. Mather, Editor

GRAPHIC METHODS IN
STRUCTURAL GEOLOGY

GRAPHIC METHODS IN STRUCTURAL GEOLOGY

BY

William L. Donn

CITY COLLEGE
OF NEW YORK

AND

John A. Shimer

BROOKLYN COLLEGE

NEW YORK

APPLETON-CENTURY-CROFTS, INC.

PRINTED IN THE UNITED STATES OF AMERICA

E–27043

PREFACE

THIS BOOK attempts to provide a useful and fairly complete discussion of the common graphic procedures used for solving problems in structural geology. Although written primarily for the undergraduate student, the book may also provide a convenient reference for the graduate student as well as the professional geologist.

Part I is intended to serve as a review of descriptive principles and an introduction to the interpretation of geologic maps and sections. Parts II and III deal with the quantitative graphic procedures which are essentially aspects of descriptive geometry applied to geologic problems. Although there is nothing particularly new added to this treatment, we believe that a book devoted only to this subject fills a definite gap encountered by the authors and probably others as well.

W. L. D.
J. A. S.

CONTENTS

PREFACE   V

Part I
DESCRIPTIVE STUDY OF BEDDED ROCKS

1. Geologic Illustration   2
2. Horizontal Structure   6
3. Tilted Structure   12
4. Folded Structure   24
5. Faulted Structure   36
6. Unconformities   54
7. Intrusive Contacts   58

Part II
QUANTITATIVE GRAPHIC PROCEDURES:
ORTHOGRAPHIC PROJECTION

8. Elements of Orthographic Projection   60
9. Structure Contours   64
10. True and Apparent Dip   68
11. Dip and Strike from Three Points   74
12. Strike and Dip from Drill-Core Data   84
13. Thickness and Depth of Strata   94
14. Completion of Areal Outcrop Patterns 100
15. Intersecting Surfaces; Plunge and Pitch; Lineation . . 102
16. Solution of Fault Problems 107

Part III
QUANTITATIVE GRAPHIC PROCEDURES:
STEREOGRAPHIC PROJECTION

17. Stereographic Projection and the Stereonet 126
18. True and Apparent Dip 132
19. Strike and Dip from Vertical Drill-Core Data 138
20. Intersecting Surfaces; Plunge and Pitch; Lineation . . 140
21. Nonrotational Faults 144

22. Problems Involving Rotation of the Sphere of Projection About a Horizontal Axis 150
23. Problems Involving Rotation of the Sphere of Projection About an Inclined Axis 160

APPENDIX
  A. Construction of an Ellipse 168
  B. Alignment Diagrams 171
  C. Selected Bibliography 176
INDEX 179

PART I

Descriptive Study of
Bedded Rocks

THE INTERPRETATION OF geologic maps depends largely upon a proper appreciation of types of contacts between rock units and how the appearance of these contacts varies as a result of differences in structure and surface topography. In other words, outcrop patterns that appear on geologic maps result from two factors: (1) the structure (horizontal, tilted, folded, and so forth), and (2) the nature of the erosional surface present. On flat surfaces all structural types yield relatively simple outcrop patterns. These patterns can become complex when an erosional surface, irregular in form and depth, is present. An understanding of certain basic principles makes possible the interpretation of geologic maps with their varied and often complex patterns.

CHAPTER 1

Geologic Illustration

A MAJOR PROBLEM CONFRONTING the geologist is the satisfactory illustration of a three-dimensional situation using a two-dimensional surface. Three convenient modes of illustration are commonly used: the *block diagram,* the *geologic map,* and the *geologic or structure section.*

Block Diagram

Block diagrams commonly used in geologic illustration show a surface and two vertical sectional views, thereby giving a three-dimensional picture. To give true perspective, lines extending away from the reader converge toward a vanishing point. Figure 1A illustrates such a one-point perspective block diagram of an eroded synclinal fold. The corners of a block may be truncated to give additional vertical sections (Figure 1B). Clearly, all surfaces of the block except the front are distorted. Two vanishing points may be used giving a two-point perspective block diagram, as in Figure 1C. Here, all surfaces are distorted from perspective. Thus, although the block is excellent for illustrative purposes, it cannot be used when accurate solutions are required. For this purpose, the geologic map and geologic section must be used.

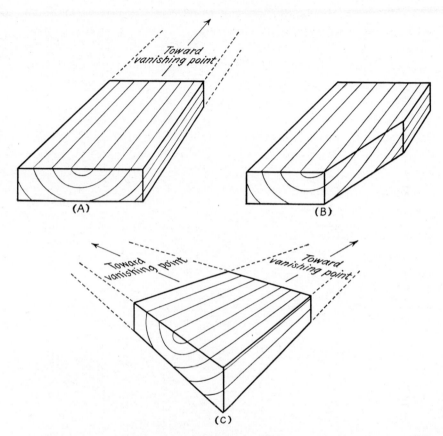

Fig. 1. Common types of block diagrams: (A) one-point perspective; (B) one-point perspective with corner truncated; (C) two-point perspective.

Geologic Map

A geologic map shows the distribution of rock formations at the earth's surface. Although this map shows the effects of relief upon the pattern of rock outcrops, the relief itself is not depicted. In general, American geologic maps show the rock pattern as it would appear if the soil cover, where present, were removed. The formations are distinguished by color, or appropriate symbols, or both. In common with all maps, they indicate all compass directions as well as a scale of distance. The top of a geologic map is conventionally toward the north. The size, shape, and distribution of various rock units are replicas of their appearance on the earth's surface.

Geologic or Structure Section

This is a section that shows the arrangement of the rock units in a vertical plane extending below the earth's surface. As the geologic map shows only two dimensions, structure sections are used commonly in conjunction with them to show the third, or depth, dimension. The top line of a structure section corresponds to a line on the earth's surface, the location of which is usually shown on the appropriate geologic map. Any number of sections can be drawn with different orientations for a given area. Except for horizontal or massive rock, the structure will have a different appearance on each differently oriented section.

A common way of illustrating a geologic map and section in combination is to imagine the vertical section rotated or folded up into the horizontal or map plane in much the same manner that the sides of a cardboard box can be rotated into the plane of the box top. Figure 2A indicates a block showing the surface *ABCD* and four numbered vertical sections. Figure 2B illustrates this block with the sections rotated into the horizontal. *ABCD* is now the undistorted geologic map, and *1, 2, 3,* and *4* are the undistorted side sections. In practice, the sections are usually separated from the map as in Figure 2C, which shows a map and four sections having the same geology given above in Figure 1. The dots here connect lines which are identical. Sections may be constructed at any orientation, for example, the northeast-southwest section (*AC*) in Figure 2D.

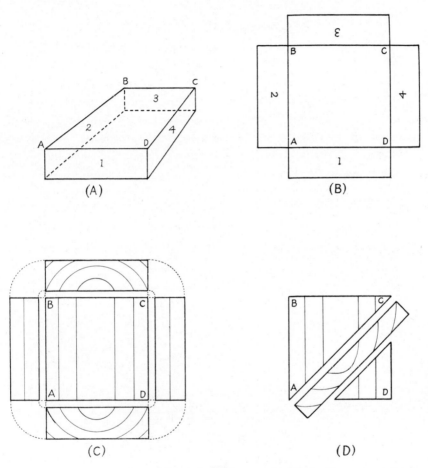

Fig. 2. Illustrations showing relationships among block diagram, geologic map, and geologic section.

CHAPTER 2

Horizontal Structure

HORIZONTAL STRUCTURE INVOLVES rocks essentially parallel to the horizon plane. This structure underlies plains and plateaus. A newly uplifted plain or plateau would show essentially one rock layer at the surface—the youngest. Complications of the surface geology, as expressed on geologic maps, are for the most part a result of erosion. The deeper the erosion, the greater will be the number of layers exposed to view. The outcrop pattern of horizontal rocks exposed by erosion conforms to the shape of the erosional form as illustrated in Figure 3, which utilizes both block diagrams and geologic maps. The map in Figure 3D actually shows the outcrop pattern most commonly found on a plain or plateau undergoing stream erosion.

BLOCK DIAGRAMS

GEOLOGIC MAPS

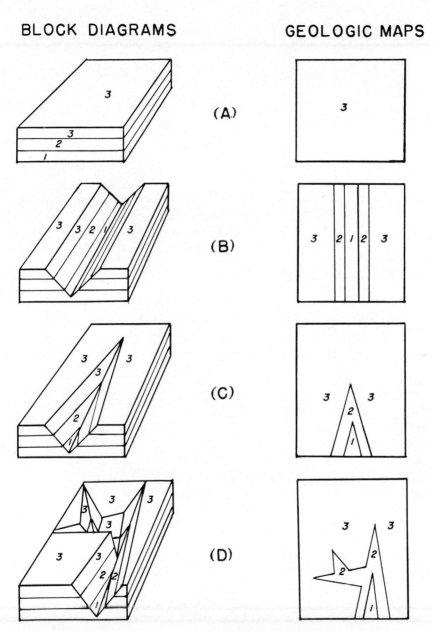

Fig. 3. Outcrop patterns of eroded horizontal structure: (A) uneroded horizontal rocks; (B) river valley with very gentle gradient; (C) river valley with steep gradient; (D) tributary valleys.

Figure 4 is a simplified tracing of the geology taken from the northern portion of the Clarion Quadrangle, Pennsylvania. The region represented is part of the Allegheny Plateau to the west of the folded Appalachian Mountain belt. The gradient of the Clarion River is gentle here, and the valley has a uniform width. Consequently, the outcrop pattern parallels the course of this main stream and conforms to the generalized case shown in Figure 3B.

The tributaries to the Clarion River have a much steeper gradient, and their valleys narrow quite rapidly away from the point of confluence with the main stream. Here the outcrop pattern forms V's which point upstream, conforming to the generalized scheme illustrated in Figure 3C. The contacts between horizontal formations are always parallel to topographic contours. Hence, in stream valleys, horizontal rock contacts always point upstream, just as do contour lines.

Generalized Graphic Procedures

Much of the work of the geologist deals with the preparation and study of an accurate descriptive picture of the structural geology of a given area. This can be accomplished readily by using standard graphic procedures without regard to accurate scales or angles. Generalized geologic sections, giving a good picture of subsurface structure, can be constructed from a geologic map, although scale, angles, and thicknesses may be only relative. Conversely, a geologic map can be drawn from an accurate geologic section, assuming uniform structure exists. However, this latter procedure must take into account topography as well as structure, and as this involves quantitative procedures, the treatment of such a problem is reserved for Part II. The procedure for constructing a section from a geologic map is outlined below.

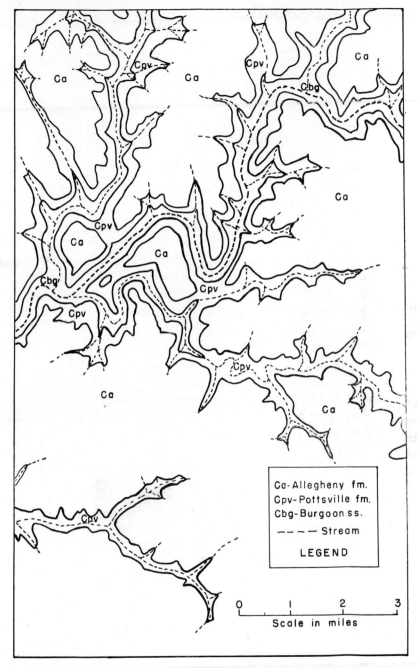

Fig. 4.   Simplified geologic map of the northern part of the Clarion Quadrangle, Pennsylvania.

Example: Given the geologic map (ABCD) of a region of horizontal rocks (Figure 5), draw a west-east and a north-south geologic (structure) section along the lines AD and CD, respectively.

Clearly, in the case of horizontal rocks, the presence of different rock formations showing on a geologic map indicates an irregular surface resulting from erosion; otherwise only a single formation would show.

1. Draw a west-east section (A'D'PO) showing five uneroded horizontal layers, because five layers show on the map. The beds were assumed here to be of equal thickness.

2. By means of dotted lines (projection lines) connect points on the section which are coincident with points on the line AD. These points on the section can be found precisely as they represent points along the profile that correspond to precisely located contacts on the map. Note, however, that the three points marking the center and sides of the valley must be approximated, as they are not formation contacts. Further, the dotted projection lines must always be perpendicular to the line on the map along which the section is taken and to the horizontal line at the top of the section.

3. Connect the points just found on the section, as shown by the heavy line. (Note that this line is the true top of the section and shows the relief which the geologic map cannot indicate.)

4. The simpler north-south section along CD is constructed by the same procedure.

EXERCISES

1. Draw a north-south geologic section along the line XY in Figure 5.

2. Draw a geologic section along the line AB on the map in Figure 6 and a block diagram of the area as viewed from the south. (Remember that this is horizontal structure.) Formation 1 is the oldest bed, and successive numbers represent successively younger beds. This common convention will be used throughout the book. Again, following common convention, north will always be toward the top of any map where directions are not specified.

3. A region of five horizontal rock units is cut by an east-west, V-shaped valley of uniform width and depth. The stream is flowing on bed 1. Draw the geologic map and a north-south structure section.

4. Draw a geologic map of a plateau with a square-shaped mesa in the center of the area. The mesa has steep but not vertical sides on which three formations can be seen.

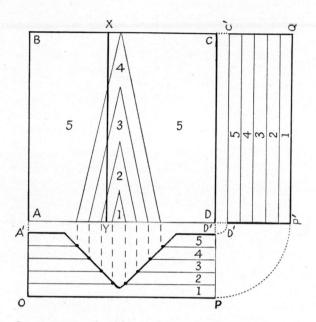

Fig. 5.   Construction of profile and section from simple geologic map.

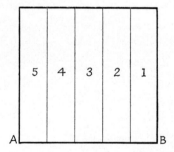

Fig. 6.   Geologic map for use with Exercise 2.

CHAPTER 3

Tilted Structure

TILTED ROCKS HAVE GENERALLY resulted from the deformation of originally horizontal rock units. They may also be the result of differential compaction or of deposition on an inclined surface, such as the gently sloping continental shelf or, more locally, the flanks of a submerged hill. The measured angle of dip can vary from a fraction of a degree up to 90 degrees. Areas of gentle dip are usually very broad, such as coastal plains, whereas areas of steep dip are much more limited, such as the regions flanking many mountain ranges.

Strike and Dip

The position in space of tilted rocks is given by means of *strike* and *dip*. Strike is the compass direction of a horizontal line on a dipping bed, or is the trend of the outcrop of a dipping bed across a flat erosional surface. The dip of a rock layer is the angle and direction at which a bed slopes beneath the horizontal. This angle is always measured in a vertical plane perpendicular to the direction of strike. Figure 7 illustrates the relation between strike and dip. The strike of the dipping layers, as measured most easily on the resistant bed, is north-south. The direction of dip is due east, and the angle of dip, which is measured in a vertical plane perpendicular to the strike (in this case, a west-east plane), is 30 degrees. Note that a statement of dip must include the direction toward which a bed dips as well as the angle of dip. Note also that when the direction of dip is given specifically, as well as the angle of dip, the strike is implicit in such a description. For example, if the dip is stated as 30 degrees due south, then the strike, which is perpendicular to the direction of dip, must be east-west. Figure 8

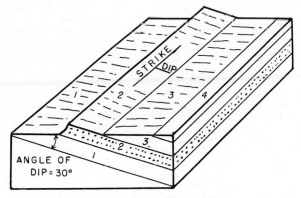

Fig. 7.   Illustration of *strike* and *dip* of tilted or dipping strata.

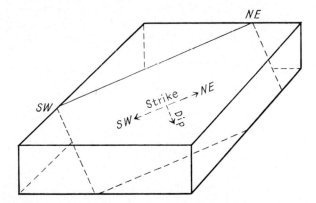

Fig. 8.   Illustration of a bed which strikes NE-SW and dips SE.

shows a bed which strikes northeast-southwest and dips to the
southeast. If the dip only is given as being toward southeast, then
the strike must of necessity be northeast-southwest. A more de-
tailed discussion of strike and dip is given in Chapter 10.

Geologic Relations and Outcrop Patterns

Age Relations. In a sequence of tilted beds, which have not been
overturned, the direction of dip is always toward younger layers.
This is a fundamental relationship which becomes obvious upon
inspection of any tilted structure, for example, that in Figure 7.
Here the beds are illustrated as dipping east, the direction in

which successively younger beds are found. In the interpretation of maps involving tilted or folded rocks this relationship is of primary importance.

Width of Outcrop. The total width of surface exposure (outcrop) of dipping beds depends on (1) the angle of dip, (2) the slope of the topographic surface, and (3) the thickness of the beds. The effects of items 1 and 2 are obvious from an examination of Figures 9 and 10, respectively, where all layers shown have the same thickness. Clearly, if the thickness changed, the width of surface exposure would vary proportionally.

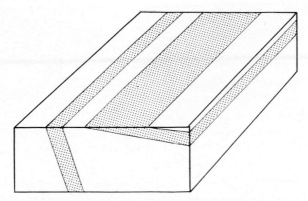

Fig. 9.   Relationship between width of outcrop and angle of dip.

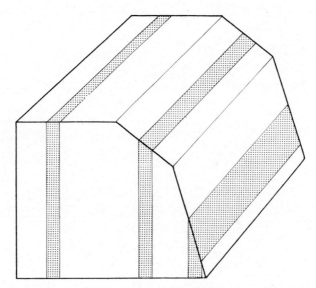

Fig. 10.   Relationship between width of outcrop and topography.

Migration of Outcrop. Note the general outcrop pattern on the block in Figure 7, the top of which represents an erosional surface. On surfaces such as this it is evident that dipping beds outcrop as parallel linear bands. If certain of the beds are more resistant than others, these will project as linear ridges as indicated by the single resistant bed illustrated in Figure 7. In general, such a linear pattern is a consequence of erosion either to a flat surface or to a ridged surface on which the erosional forms are parallel to the strike, as occurs from erosion by subsequent streams. However,

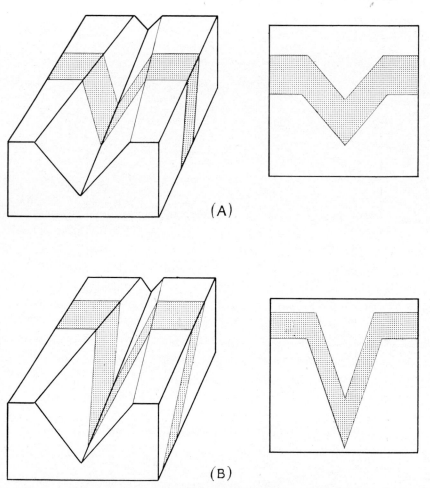

(A)

(B)

Fig. 11. Migration of outcrop of dipping beds resulting from stream erosion: (A) dip of bed greatly exceeds gradient of stream; (B) dip of bed barely exceeds gradient of stream.

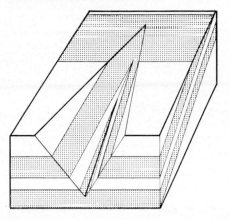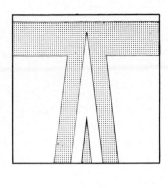

Fig. 12.   Migration of outcrop where beds dip in same direction but more
gently than gradient of stream.

when stream valleys are transverse to the strike, this simple outcrop pattern becomes modified. The most common modification is
illustrated in Figures 11A and 11B, in which the dip of the beds
exceeds the stream gradient. Where cut by the stream valley the
outcrop pattern, as shown by formational contacts, is V-shaped.
The V is produced because the outcrop of the beds migrates in the
direction of dip when eroded. Clearly, the deeper the erosion the
greater is the displacement, which is greatest at the valley floor.
We can now deduce the following general rule (sometimes called
the *Rule of V's*): *where dipping beds are eroded by a transverse
stream valley, the V's point in the direction of dip.*

We can also deduce that the amount of migration, as measured
by the length of the V's, depends on the depth of erosion, as noted
above, and also the angle of dip of the beds. The deeper the erosion, the greater is the amount of migration, and the gentler the
dip, the greater is the amount of migration. The latter is obvious
from the comparison of Figures 11A and 11B.

It should also be clear that the V's point in the direction of dip
in these cases and do not depend on the direction of stream flow.
The Rule of V's does not apply, however, where the stream flows in
the direction of dip of the beds and has a gradient greater than the
dip. Such relations may exist in plain or plateau areas where the
beds are not quite horizontal. Where such gently dipping beds are
crossed by a stream valley whose gradient is steeper than the dip,
the erosional V's actually point up-dip, as illustrated in Figure 12.

Figure 13 shows a simplified tracing of the geologic map of the north-central portion of the Apishapa Quadrangle, Colorado. This area is in south-central Colorado, just east of the Rocky Mountain Front Range. The formations dip gently northeastward, away from the mountains, and show a definite northwest-southeast trend indicative of the strike. This direction of dip is clear because the younger formations lie to the northeast, and the V's in the stream valleys also point this way. Although the relative ages of the beds can be determined from the legend (a necessary feature of geologic maps), they also become obvious once the direction of dip is determined.

Note the contact between the Timpas limestone (Kt) and the Apishapa shale (Ka) at the Apishapa River. This contact is displaced about a mile and a half to the northeast in a prominent V from the erosional effect of the river valley. A topographic map of the same region shows the valley to be about 225 feet deep here. Thus the outcrops of the beds have migrated about one and a half miles as the result of erosion to this depth. The slope of the beds necessary to produce this migration is consequently about 150 feet per mile. As a slope of 93 feet per mile is equal to one degree for gently dipping beds, this formation dips at slightly over one and one-half degrees. The geologic section shown with the map exaggerates the dip somewhat for illustration purposes.

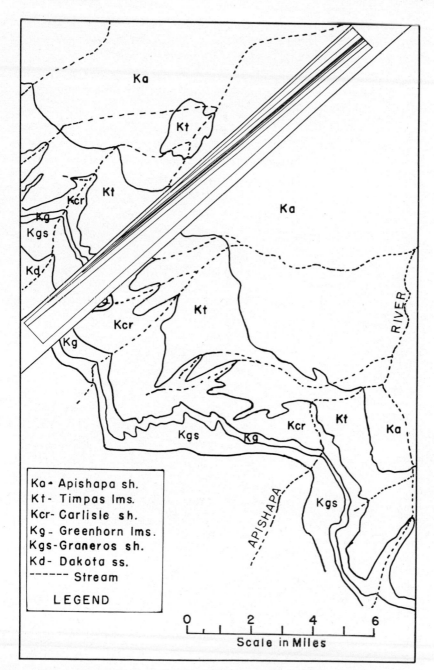

Fig. 13. Simplified geologic map of the north-central part of the Apishapa Quadrangle, Colorado.

Compare the Apishapa geology with that shown in Figure 14, which illustrates the outcrop pattern of more steeply dipping beds from a region within the Central Rocky Mountains (central part of the Dayton Quadrangle, Wyoming). The scale of this map is the same as that of the preceding one. Note Rapid Creek in the southeastern quarter of our map. In crossing Rapid Creek the contact between the Deadwood formation (Cd) and Madison limestone (Cm) is displaced in a V toward the northeast for a distance of half a mile in a descent of 2000 feet. This corresponds to a dip of about 40 degrees at this place. However, the dip decreases toward the northeast as is evident from the increasing length of the V's and the broad exposure of the De Smet formation (Kds).

Note also the scalloped pattern of the Amsden formation (Ca) produced by the numerous closely spaced valleys resulting in narrow stream divides. In cases like this be sure to determine the direction of the V where the outcrop crosses the stream, rather than where it crosses the divide between streams. Of course, the direction of dip may be determined equally well from the outcrop displacement in crossing a divide or hill, so long as it is realized that displacement in this case is opposite to the direction of dip.

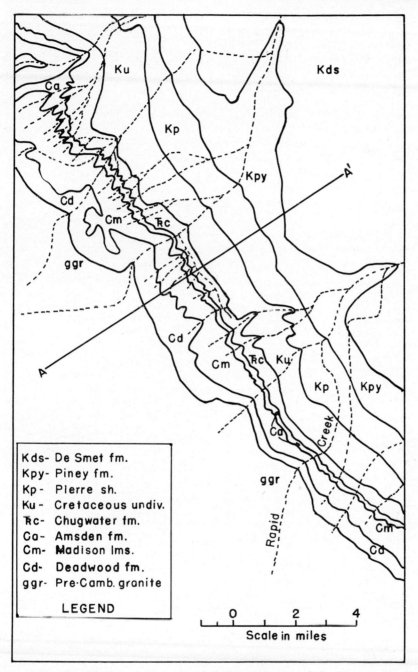

Kds- De Smet fm.
Kpy- Piney fm.
Kp - Pierre sh.
Ku - Cretaceous undiv.
Rc- Chugwater fm.
Ca- Amsden fm.
Cm- Madison lms.
Cd- Deadwood fm.
ggr- Pre-Camb. granite

LEGEND

0   2   4

Scale in miles

Fig. 14.   Simplified geologic map of the central part of the Dayton Quadrangle, Wyoming.

EXERCISES

1. **Example. The geologic map in Figure 15, shows five beds out-cropping on a flat erosional surface. Relative ages are shown by numbers. Construct north-south and east-west structure sections.**

The surface is flat, and the beds outcrop as linear bands; therefore the structure must consist of tilted rocks. The strike is obviously east-west, and the dip is due south in the direction of successively younger beds. The north-south section is thus in a plane perpendicular to the strike, and the attitude of the beds will show the actual dip. In the east-west section, which is parallel to the strike, the beds will not show any dip.

Following the general procedure given previously with horizontal structure, construct the blank section, $D'C'OP$. Project formational contact points from the side of the map along DC to the top of the section $D'C'$ as shown. Then, assuming any convenient dip angle (as none is given here) draw the formations dipping to the south on the section. Keep formation contacts parallel if you have no reason to suspect that the beds converge or diverge with depth.

Note well: The section $D'C'OP$ *is in a vertical plane. The line* $C'D'$ *is a horizontal line at the surface, identical with* CD *on the map.* PO *is a horizontal line vertically beneath* $D'C'$, *and beds 1–5 dip due south, not southeast.*

Draw the section $A'D'MN$, having the same depth as the north-south section. Remember that $A'D'$ is coincident with AD, and $D'M$ is coincident with $D'P$. Thus formational contacts along $D'P$ can also be found at the same depths on line $D'M$. Draw the horizontal formational boundaries on this section, starting with the appropriate points on line $D'M$. It should be noted that the depth to which the section is taken is arbitrary in this treatment.

2. Draw a block diagram of the situation in problem 1.

3. Complete the outcrop pattern across the stream valley on the geologic map in Figure 16. Assume the surface to be flat except for a V-shaped valley. Also draw a west-east structure section, assuming a uniform dip of 45 degrees.

4. Draw a section along the line AA' in Figure 14, showing clearly the decreasing dip to the northeast and the nonconformity between the Deadwood formation and the granite.

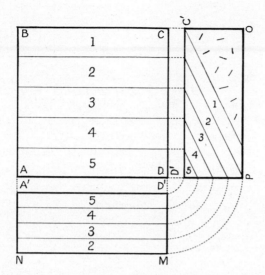

Fig. 15.   Construction of geologic sections from a simple geologic map of
tilted strata.

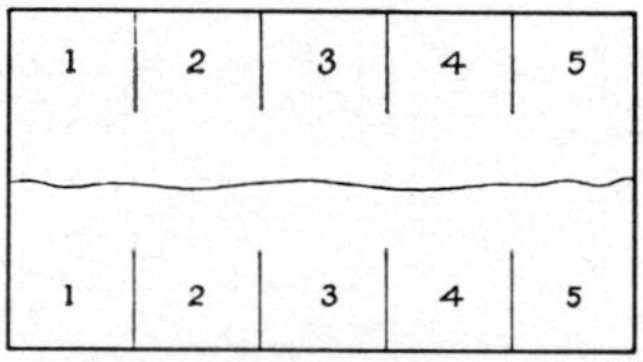

Fig. 16.   Incomplete geologic map of tilted strata for use with Exercise 3.

CHAPTER 4

Folded Structure

A FOLD CAN BE CONSIDERED as a structural unit consisting of two sets of dipping beds. In the case of an anticline the sets dip in opposite directions away from the fold axis, whereas for a syncline the beds dip toward the axis. Therefore all of the rules concerned with tilted beds (age relations, width of outcrop, and direction and amount of migration) apply to the interpretation of folded beds.

When a fold is considered as a unit there are further relationships of importance in the interpretation of the structure. A consideration of the most fundamental descriptive elements of folds necessary to interpretation of structure is reviewed first.

Description and Nomenclature of Folds

Many of the chief elements of folds are illustrated in Figure 17A, which shows two uneroded anticlines and an intervening syncline, and 17B, which shows the same area eroded to a flat surface. The planes *ABCD* and *MNOP* are the axial planes of the anticline and syncline, respectively. Note that the axial planes divide the folds into equal halves. The intersection of the axial plane with any bedding surface gives a line called the axis. Thus, *AB*, *XY*, and actually any lines parallel to these in the plane *ABCD* are axes of the anticline. Line *MN* is an axis of the syncline. Note that the strike of a fold axis gives the directional trend of the entire fold structure.

The sides of folds are called limbs or flanks. Because adjacent folds have limbs in common, *AMPD* represents the east limb of the anticline as well as the west limb of the syncline.

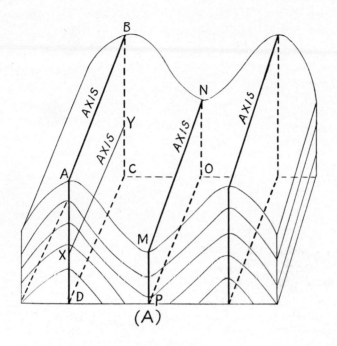

(A)

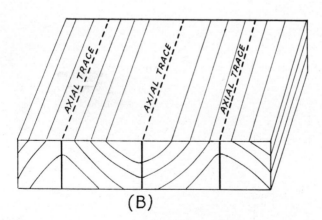

(B)

Fig. 17. Block diagrams of uneroded and eroded folds having horizontal
axes and vertical axial planes.

In Figure 18, the limbs of the folds have different angles of dip. Such folds are said to be asymmetrical in contrast to the symmetrical folds in Figure 17. Note that the axial plane of an asymmetrical fold is not vertical but leans toward the steeper flank of an anticline (or the gentler flank of a syncline).

Figure 19 illustrates overturned folds, that is, folds having the beds of one limb turned through an angle of more than 90 degrees, with the result that both flanks dip in the same direction (although rarely at the same angle). In the overturned limb the beds are inverted, that is, younger beds underlie older, and the tops of beds lie below the bottoms.

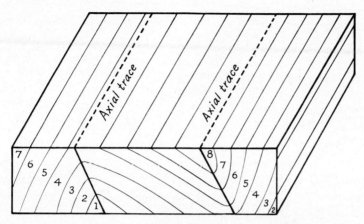

Fig. 18.   Block diagram of asymmetric folds showing the inclination of the
axial planes.

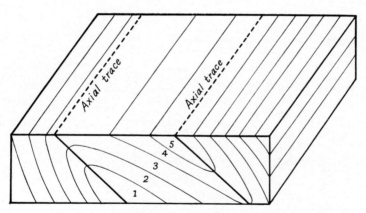

Fig. 19.   Block diagram showing overturned folds.

The axes of all of the folds pictured so far are horizontal. Compare Figures 20A and 20B. The axis of the fold in 20A is also horizontal, but the axis of the fold in 20B is inclined to the horizontal. A fold whose axis is not horizontal is said to plunge. The angle of inclination of the axis measured in the vertical plane which includes the axis is the *angle of plunge* or simply *plunge*. Note that the folds illustrated in Figure 20 are symmetrical with vertical axial planes.

In cases where plunging folds are either asymmetric or overturned the axial planes are inclined, and another important fold element is introduced, namely, *pitch*. Note Figure 21, in which plane *ABCD* is the inclined axial plane of a plunging asymmetric anticline. Line *AO* is an axis of the fold. Plane *AEFG* is a vertical plane which includes the axis. Angle *EAO* is the plunge, because it is the angle between the axis and the horizontal measured in a vertical plane. The angle *BAO*, which is the angle between the axis and the horizontal, measured in the inclined axial plane, is the pitch. (Pitch, in general, is defined as the angle between a line in an inclined plane and the horizontal, measured in the inclined plane.)

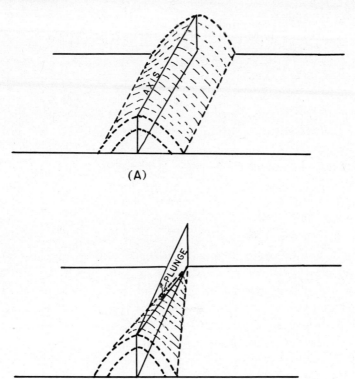

(A)

(B)

Fig. 20. Comparison of (A) horizontal with (B) plunging folds.

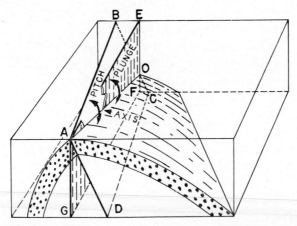

Fig. 21. Illustration of *plunge* and *pitch* for a plunging asymmetric fold.

Outcrop Pattern of Folds

Folds with Horizontal Axes. On a flat erosional surface the outcrop pattern of such folds consists of parallel linear bands. See Figures 17B, 18, and 19. Note particularly that there is a symmetrical repetition of beds about any fold axis. The oldest exposed beds in an eroded anticline lie along the anticlinal axis, whereas the youngest beds in an eroded syncline lie along the axis. Beds dip away from an anticlinal axis and toward a synclinal axis, following the rule that beds dip toward younger layers. The outcrop of the same bed on opposite sides of the axis of a symmetrical fold shows the same width. Because the width of outcrop varies with the angle of dip, the outcrop of a given bed on opposite sides of an asymmetric fold shows different widths. Compare Figure 17B with Figures 18 and 19 for an illustration of this effect. Parallel linear ridges and valleys are commonly found in areas where fold structure exists and has been eroded by subsequent streams.

If stream valleys or other erosional features are developed transverse to the strike, the linear outcrop pattern becomes distorted. This is a result of the migration of outcrop down the dip, as in the case of simple tilted layers described earlier, and is pictured schematically in Figure 22, which shows a block diagram and geologic map of the same area.

Folds with Plunging Axes. The outcrop pattern of eroded plunging folds shows converging rather than essentially parallel contacts. This can be seen from a study of Figure 23, which illustrates two plunging anticlines with an intervening syncline. Both the uneroded and eroded folds are shown. It is obvious that the outcrop of the beds converges to a *nose* in the direction of plunge of the anticline, whereas the direction of convergence or nose of a plunging syncline is opposite to the direction of plunge. The differential erosion of such structures produces *zig-zag ridges*. All other rules of outcrop behavior explained for folds with horizontal axes—that is, age relations, width of outcrop, and migration of outcrop—apply equally to plunging folds.

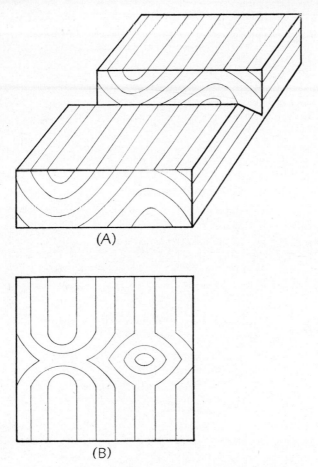

(A)

(B)

Fig. 22. Outcrop pattern of folded strata eroded by a transverse stream as shown on (A) block diagram and (B) geologic map.

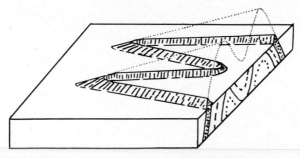

Fig. 23. Block diagram showing the outcrop pattern of a single resistant formation in a series of eroded plunging folds. The restored, uneroded resistant layer is also illustrated.

A simplified tracing of part of a geologic map of the Gadsden Quadrangle, Alabama, is shown in Figure 24. The principal feature consists of essentially parallel bands of outcrop with the oldest formation in the center. A similar sequence of progressively younger beds occurs on either side. Such an arrangement indicates an anticline having a horizontal axis which runs along the middle of the outcrop pattern of the Knox Dolomite (Sk), the oldest unit. The width of outcrop of similar formations is broader on the southeast than on the northwest flank of the fold, indicating the anticline to be asymmetric, with the limb of gentler dip to the southeast. The V's in the transverse valleys point away from the axis and thus also indicate the anticlinal nature of the structure. They show that the beds dip away from the fold axis, or in the direction of younger layers. In the case of a syncline the V's would point toward the axis.

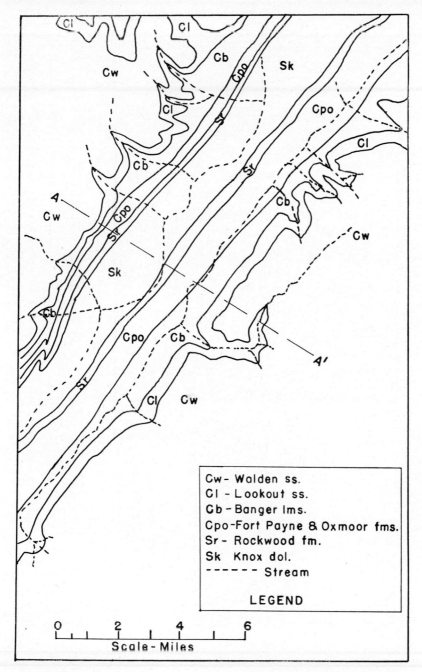

Cw - Walden ss.
Cl - Lookout ss.
Cb - Banger lms.
Cpo - Fort Payne & Oxmoor fms.
Sr - Rockwood fm.
Sk Knox dol.
- - - - - Stream

LEGEND

0   2   4   6
Scale - Miles

Fig. 24.   Simplified geologic map of part of the Gadsden Quadrangle,
Alabama.

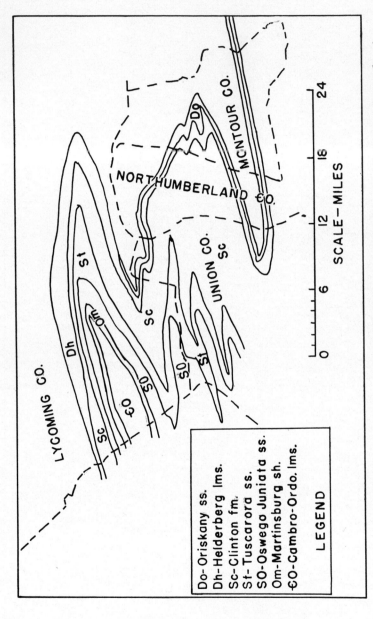

Fig. 25.   Generalized geologic map of a part of the Appalachian Mountains in central Pennsylvania.

Figure 25 is a generalized geologic map of portions of Lycoming, Union, and Northumberland counties in Pennsylvania. The zig-zag pattern indicates a series of plunging synclines and anticlines. By means of the legend, which gives formation ages, it is possible to distinguish the anticlines from the synclines and thus determine the direction of the plunge.

EXERCISES

1. Draw a west-east structure section along line AA' shown in the geologic map in Figure 26. Consider *1* the oldest layer.

2. Complete the outcrop pattern in the stream valley in Figure 26.

3. Draw a block diagram of two anticlines and one syncline plunging north and eroded to a flat surface. Show at least seven formations.

4. Draw a section along line AA' in Figure 24. Specific dip values are not given.

5. Locate the anticlines and synclines in Figure 25. Which way does each plunge?

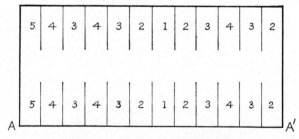

Fig. 26.   Incomplete geologic map of eroded folds for use with Exercise 2.

CHAPTER 5

Faulted Structure

OUR PURPOSE HERE IS to show the ways in which faults affect outcrop patterns of bedded rocks. This treatment, which emphasizes the results of the faulting of tilted structures, may for the most part be applied equally well to the faulting of fold structures. The only outcrop modification of nonrotational faulting of horizontal rocks is indicated in Figure 27, which shows a block diagram of an eroded region following faulting. Note that the only significant change is that beds of different ages are adjacent to each other along the fault line. Many *intersecting* faults can complicate this pattern which otherwise is quite simple.

The effect of faulting on the outcrop pattern of tilted beds depends on three factors:

1. The relation between the strike of the fault plane and the strike of the beds. (The fault plane may have the same strike as the beds—a *strike fault*—or it may cut across the beds at some angle up to 90 degrees—a *transverse fault*.)

2. The relation between the angle and direction of dip of the fault plane and the angle and direction of dip of the beds.

3. The nature of the motion along the fault plane.

Strike Faults

In Figure 28, which illustrates regions that have been faulted and eroded, the strike faults dip in a direction opposite to that of the beds. In Figure 28A the fault illustrated is normal, and in Figure 28B it is reverse. Note that repetition of beds occurs on opposite sides of the fault line on the map view of Figure 28A. Repetition of beds always occurs where dipping beds are cut by a normal strike fault which dips in the opposite direction to the dip of the beds. Where the strike fault is reverse, as in Figure 28B, an omission of beds occurs. Note that bed *4* does not outcrop any-

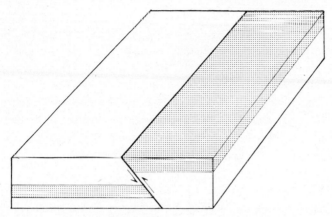

Fig. 27.   Block diagram showing horizontal rocks which have been faulted
and eroded to a level surface.

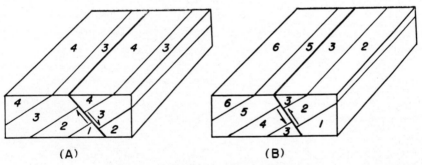

(A)   (B)

Fig. 28.   (A) repetition of beds following erosion of a region of tilted layers
cut by a normal strike fault which dips opposite to the beds; (B) omission
of beds following erosion of a region of tilted layers cut by a reverse strike
fault which dips opposite to the beds.

where on the surface in this case. The thickness of the omitted
unit(s) depends on the amount of displacement, as well as on the
angle of the dip of both beds and fault; this also is true for the thickness of the repeated rocks illustrated in Figure 28A.

The sequences in Figure 29A, B, C, and D illustrate outcrop patterns resulting from the erosion of tilted layers cut by strike faults dipping in the same direction as the beds. In Figures 29A and 29B the fault dips more steeply than the beds. In such cases, the normal fault always produces omission, as illustrated in Figure 29A, and the reverse fault always yields repetition, as illustrated in Figure 29B. In Figures 29C and 29D the faults dip more gently than the beds. In such cases, the normal fault always produces repetition, as illustrated in Figure 29C, and the reverse fault gives omission, as illustrated in Figure 29D.

Vertical strike faults having movement not parallel to the bedding always result in either repetition or omission. In summary, repetition of beds occurs for (1) normal faults which dip opposite to the beds, (2) normal faults which dip in the same direction but gentler than the beds, and (3) reverse faults which dip in the same direction but steeper than the beds. Omission occurs for (1) normal faults which dip in the same direction but steeper than the beds (2) reverse faults which dip in the same direction but gentler than the beds, and (3) reverse faults which dip opposite to the beds. Where the fault plane is parallel to the bedding, as is common with strike faults, there is neither omission nor repetition.

It is important to realize that repetition or omission of beds in the field is positive evidence for the presence of a fault. The repetition about a fault line, in the cases of strike faults, is not symmetrical as is the repetition of beds on the opposite sides of a fold axis.

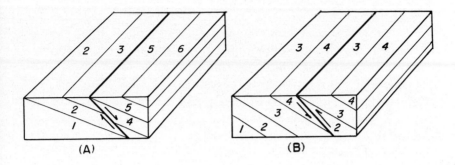

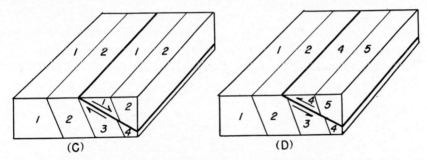

Fig. 29. Diagrams illustrating omission and repetition of beds where faults
and beds dip in the same direction.

Transverse Faults

The angle between the strike of a transverse fault and the strike of the beds may be any angle up to a right angle. Wherever a fault cuts the beds at right angles, a *simple offset* relationship results, regardless of the relative directions of dip of beds and fault, and the direction of motion in the fault plane. Simple offset is illustrated in Figure 30B which shows the outcrop pattern resulting from the erosion of an area of tilted rocks cut by a fault at right angles to the strike. Erosion of the uplifted block produces an eastward migration of the outcrop of the tilted beds. If the beds here were dipping westward instead of eastward, displacement would be to the west. Clearly, this pattern would also develop if the fault raised the south block, in which case the beds to the south would be displaced following erosion. Further, simple horizontal movement alone (tear fault) with the north block moving relatively eastward also gives the pattern illustrated. It is rarely possible for the movement along the fault plane to be parallel to the bedding, so that, following erosion, no apparent displacement would occur.

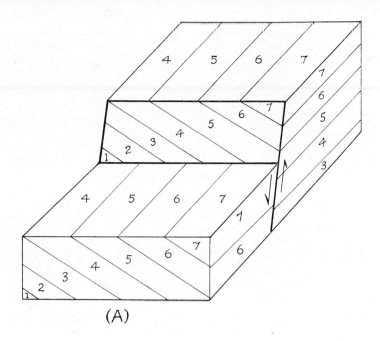

(A)

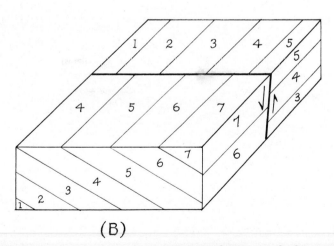

(B)

Fig. 30.   The production of *simple offset* in dipping rocks by a transverse
fault with only dip-slip motion.

If a transverse fault cuts the strike of the beds obliquely, offset with *gap* or *overlap* results, except for the rare case just described. Compare A and B of Figure 31. Following erosion, the east bed has migrated so that an overlap of outcrop occurs along the fault line. At the same time, the west bed, which dips in the opposite direction, is displaced so that a gap in outcrop occurs. It should be apparent that if the southern block were raised and eroded, the gap would appear in the east bed, and the overlap in the west bed. Either offset with gap or offset with overlap can be produced by simple horizontal movement along the fault line.

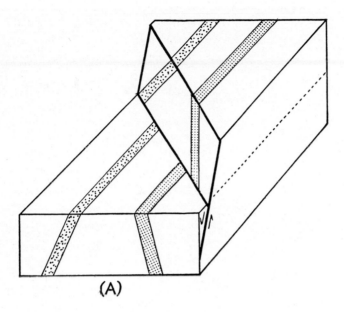

(A)

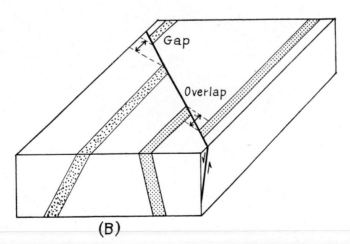

(B)

Fig. 31.   The production of *gap* or *overlap* in dipping rocks by a transverse
fault with only dip-slip motion.

Rotational Faults

The faults considered so far, which have essentially linear motion in the fault plane, do not alter the strike of the beds they displace. However, if the motion in an inclined fault plane is rotational, the strike and the dip of the beds is usually altered.

Rotational faults are shown in Figures 32 and 33. Parts A and B show the areas before and after erosion, respectively. The change of strike following faulting is obvious here. Naturally, the actual outcrop appearance in a particular case depends on the relation between the strike and dip of the beds on one hand and the strike, dip, and exact movement in the fault plane on the other hand. In special cases, such as certain vertical faults, strike may not be altered. Only in cases of rotational bedding plane faults does the dip remain unchanged; in all other cases the dip is changed. For example, in Figure 32 the dip of the bed in the eastern block is increased. If the bed were dipping north instead of south, it can be visualized readily that the dip would be decreased under the same conditions.

Any fault, if followed sufficiently far along its strike, will be found to die out or meet another fault. A fault cannot terminate abruptly without the presence of another crosscutting fault at its end.

Even faults which are essentially nonrotational must, for the most part, have some rotational movement toward their extremities. This is a consequence of the differential movement in the fault plane as the fault dies out. Obviously, the amount of rotation depends on the rapidity with which the fault motion decreases, so that the consequent effect on the outcrop pattern may be prominent or barely discernible. Where a strike fault dies out, the rotational movement causes the beds to change strike, with each bed successively converging toward the fault. Thus, Figure 33 can be considered as depicting the termination of a strike fault.

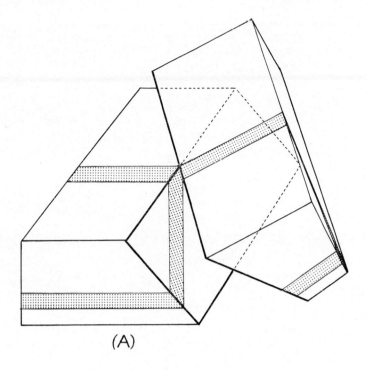

(A)

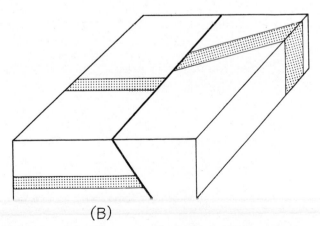

(B)

Fig. 32.   Changes in strike and dip produced by a rotational transverse fault.

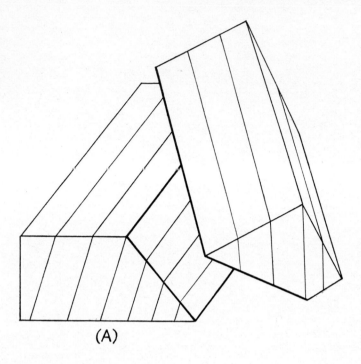

(A)

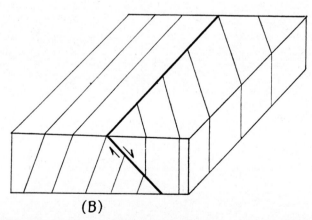

(B)

Fig. 33.　Changes in strike and dip produced by a rotational strike fault.

Figure 34 illustrates a reverse strike fault which has produced an omission of beds. Note the manner in which the missing beds reappear at the surface as the fault displacement decreases. The difference in amount of motion is shown in the two structure sections. The unfaulted beds strike north-south, as do those which have suffered maximum dislocation where the motion is essentially linear. However, it is obvious that where the fault is dying out, a rotational movement has occurred and the direction of strike has been changed.

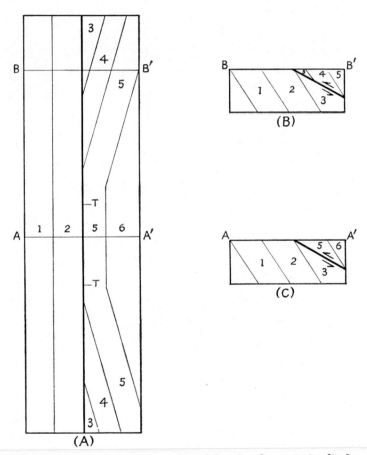

Fig. 34.   The rotational effect produced by the decrease in displacement along a strike fault as shown in the geologic map (A), and the sections (B) and (C).

Selected Illustrations

Figure 35 is a tracing of part of the geologic map of the Cleveland Quadrangle, Tennessee. The map shows prominent northeast-southwest strike faults. These faults have produced frequent repetition of the Rome formation ($\mathrm{\mathfrak{C}r}$), Connasauga shale ($\mathrm{\mathfrak{C}c}$), and the Knox dolomite (Ok). Apparently, the fault to the southeast did not have sufficient vertical motion to repeat the Rome formation. Note that this same fault, if traced to the northeast and southwest, appears to weaken, because the Connasauga shale lenses out (through rotational movement) against the fault. An asymmetric syncline plunging to the northeast is evident on the southeastern portion of the map. The age relations, determined both from the legend and the direction of dip shown by outcrop displacements across stream valleys, demonstrate the presence of this synclinal structure. The asymmetry of the syncline is shown by the greater surface width of the formations on the northwestern flank of the structure as compared to the lesser width on the southeastern flank. The accompanying geologic section gives a further clarification of the structure. Note that the reverse faults must be drawn steeper than the beds which dip in the same direction in order to produce the observed repetition.

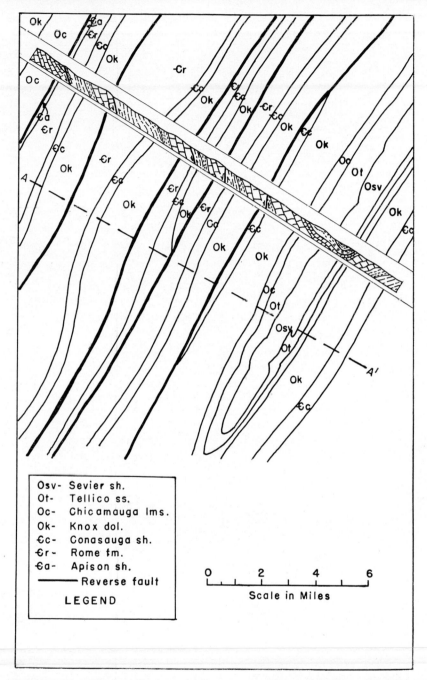

Osv- Sevier sh.
Ot- Tellico ss.
Oc- Chicamauga lms.
Ok- Knox dol.
Єc- Conasauga sh.
Єr- Rome fm.
Єa- Apison sh.
—— Reverse fault

LEGEND

0   2   4   6
Scale in Miles

Fig. 35. Simplified geologic map showing repetition of beds on the Cleveland Quadrangle, Tennessee.

Figure 36 illustrates the geologic map and a transverse geologic section which is taken from the northwest corner of the Fairfield Quadrangle, Pennsylvania. (For clarity, there is vertical exaggeration in the section.) The structure indicated by the map consists of plunging folds, as is shown by the nature of the repetition of the beds, together with the typical plunge pattern. The axes of one anticline and two synclines are marked with appropriate symbols. Two prominent strike faults are also evident. The fault to the west has a gentle dip to the southeast, as evidenced by its marked displacement toward the southeast (in stream valleys). This fault, which cuts the southeast limb of a syncline, has brought older beds on the east in contact with younger beds on the west side of the fault, thereby causing omission. The direction of dip of the fault plane, together with the relative ages of the rocks on either side of the fault, indicate that the hanging wall or east side has moved up, giving a low-angle reverse or thrust fault. Note the use of a conventional thrust fault symbol, which is always placed on the overthrust side of a thrust fault. The fault to the east must dip very steeply, as no displacement is indicated in the stream valleys. The west side of this steep fault (actually a normal fault) has moved up, as indicated by the presence of older beds on this side. Conventional normal fault symbols are used here to show relative movement.

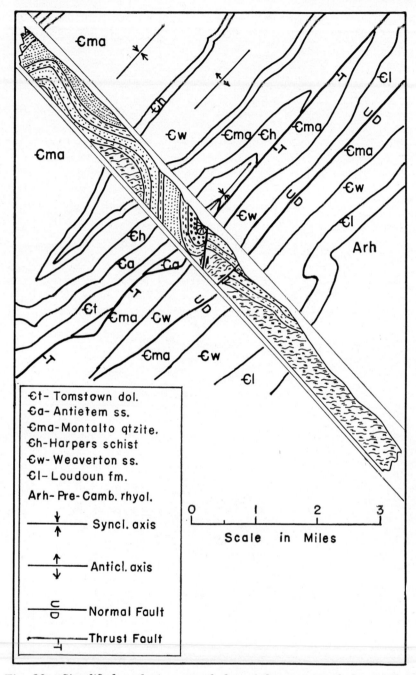

Ɛt– Tomstown dol.
Ɛa– Antietem ss.
Ɛma–Montalto qtzite.
Ɛh–Harpers schist
Ɛw– Weaverton ss.
Ɛl– Loudoun fm.

Arh– Pre- Camb. rhyol.

———— Syncl. axis

———— Anticl. axis

———— Normal Fault

———— Thrust Fault

Fig. 36.   Simplified geologic map of the northwest part of the Fairfield
Quadrangle, Pennsylvania.

Figure 37 is a tracing of the geologic map of part of the Gettysburg Quadrangle, Pennsylvania. Offset with overlap is illustrated where two normal faults cut transversely across the strike of a sill in Triassic rocks. The direction of relative movement is shown for both faults. The northwestward displacement of the sill on the upthrown blocks indicates it to be dipping to the northwest.

EXERCISES

1. Draw a geologic map illustrating the following conditions: (a) a sequence of sedimentary beds dipping west, cut by a reverse fault which dips south and strikes east-west, (b) erosion to a flat surface following faulting.

2. Draw a structure section along line AA' in Figure 35.

3. Draw a series of three block diagrams showing the region illustrated in Figure 37: (a) before faulting, (b) after faulting but before erosion, (c) after erosion to the present surface.

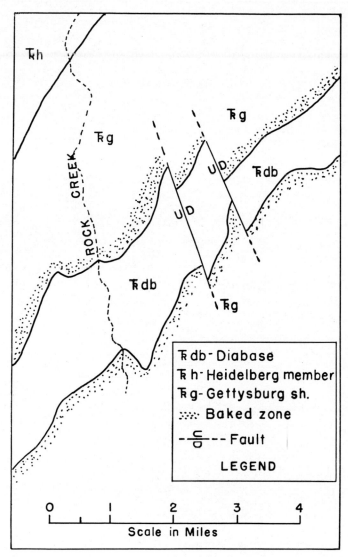

Fig. 37. Simplified geologic map of part of the Gettysburg Quadrangle, Pennsylvania.

CHAPTER 6

Unconformities

THE EXPOSURE OF EROSIONAL contacts (unconformities) may result in rather distinctive outcrop patterns in addition to those produced by the regular structural types discussed above.

The term *unconformity* as commonly used includes *disconformity, nonconformity,* and *angular unconformity.*

Disconformity

Because a disconformity is an erosional surface among bedded rocks which are parallel to each other, its effect is no different from that of a bedding plane and thus introduces no unique feature in the outcrop pattern. The presence of a disconformity is manifest by a hiatus in the sedimentary sequence. In Figure 24 the absence of Devonian rocks between the Silurian and Carboniferous indicates the presence of a disconformity. The actual disconformity is the contact between the Rockwood formation (Sr) and the Fort Payne and Oxmoor formations (Cpo) and clearly parallels the conformable formational contacts. The hiatus indicated by the disconformity implies either erosion or nondeposition of the incomplete sedimentary sequence. Actually, the effects of both may be involved.

Nonconformity

This is an erosional contact between an older massive igneous rock unit and an overlying series of younger sediments.

The contact between the Grey Granite (ggr) and the Deadwood formation (Cd) in Figure 14 is a nonconformity. This can be deduced because the granite nowhere in this area intrudes the Deadwood or other younger formations and thus is presumably older.

54

It is therefore seen that the outcrop of a nonconformity is a line which has massive igneous rock on one side and exposures of sedimentary formations, which are parallel to the nonconformity, on the other.

Angular Unconformity

This is an erosional surface which separates two sequences of layered rock in such a way that an angular relation exists between them. The layers of the younger sequence are parallel to the erosional surface, and the layers of the older underlying group meet this surface at some angle. An angular unconformity results from a geologic history involving the erosion of a deformed sequence of layered rock, with subsequent deposition of sediments upon the erosional surface. The angular unconformity may be horizontal or may be folded or tilted if further deformation occurs in the area. Figure 38 shows sectional views of the types of unconformities discussed here.

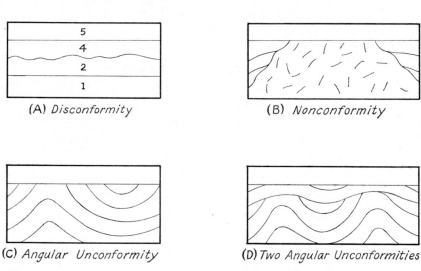

(A) *Disconformity*   (B) *Nonconformity*

(C) *Angular Unconformity*   (D) *Two Angular Unconformities*

Fig. 38.   Structure sections illustrating different types of unconformities.

Figure 39 is a simplified tracing of the geologic map of the northeast corner of the Three Forks Quadrangle, Montana. The Bozeman formation (Tb) is a horizontal rock unit which blankets and lies unconformably upon much of the pre-Tertiary folded or crystalline rocks in this area. The contact between the Bozeman and all older sedimentary beds is the outcrop of a surface of angular unconformity. Where the older rocks are massive, such as the Archean granite (ARgn), the unconformable contact would be classified as a nonconformity. Further, the contact between the granite and the Cambrian Flathead formation (€fg) is also a nonconformity. The contact between the Gallatin formation (€fg) and the Jefferson limestone (Dj) is presumably a disconformity, owing to the omission of the Ordovician and Silurian rocks. The irregular contact between the Bozeman and the sedimentary beds from Cambrian to Tertiary marks the outcrop of an angular unconformity.

EXERCISE

1. Draw structure sections along the lines *AA'* and *BB'* of Figure 39.

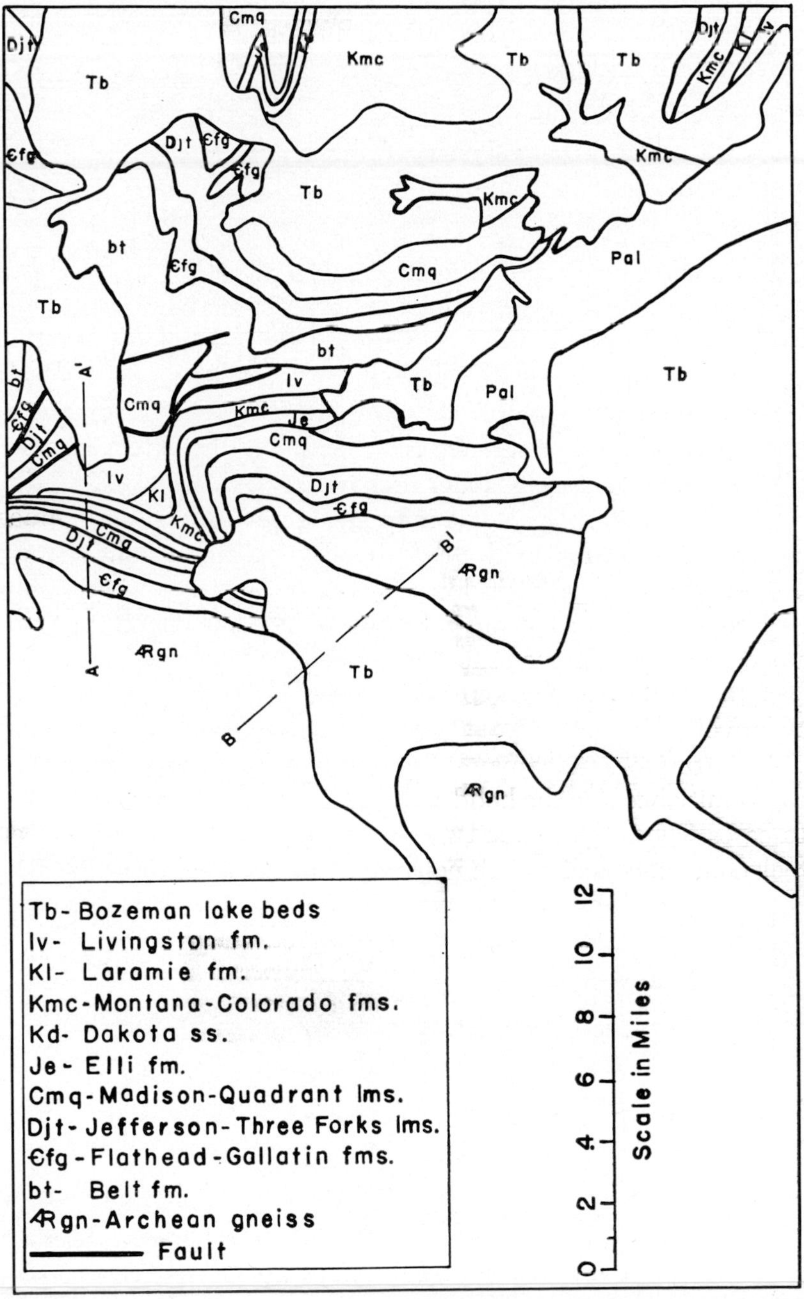
Tb- Bozeman lake beds
lv- Livingston fm.
Kl- Laramie fm.
Kmc-Montana-Colorado fms.
Kd- Dakota ss.
Je- Elli fm.
Cmq-Madison-Quadrant lms.
Djt- Jefferson-Three Forks lms.
Єfg - Flathead-Gallatin fms.
bt- Belt fm.
ARgn-Archean gneiss
Fault
Scale in Miles
0 2 4 6 8 10 12

Fig. 39. Simplified geologic map of part of the Three Forks Quadrangle, Montana.

CHAPTER 7

Intrusive Contacts

IGNEOUS INTRUSIONS MAY BE conformable with their bedded host rock, as in the cases of sills and laccoliths, or they may cut across the layered structures, as in the cases of dikes, stocks, and batho liths. The presence of conformable intrusions introduces no modifications of outcrop pattern. However, where the intrusion cuts a bedded structure, its presence is shown by a distinctive intrusive contact which cuts across older rock units.

The pattern in the geologic map in Figure 40A involves a linear intrusive contact formed by a dike cutting tilted or folded rocks. Any outcrop pattern considered heretofore may show the added feature of a tabular igneous body cutting the structure. Similarly, any outcrop pattern may show the effect of the intrusion of a stock or batholith, as in Figure 40B. The latter forms are more irregular and involve a larger area.

An intrusive contact may be definitely distinguished from a nonconformity because the bedded structures are cut by the intrusion. In cases where the bedded structures are parallel to the igneous rock contact, conceivably a nonconformity or a conformable igneous intrusive contact may be present. Field evidence may be necessary to determine the actual type of contact.

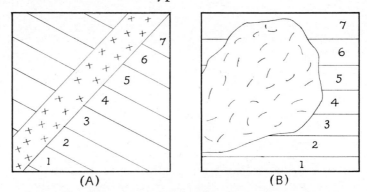

(A) (B)

Fig. 40.   Geologic maps illustrating intrusive contacts.

PART II

Quantitative Graphic Procedures:
Orthographic Projection

THE GRAPHIC METHODS OF structural geology, on the whole, are drawn from two standard projection techniques of descriptive geometry, namely orthographic and stereographic projection. There seems to be a definite advantage in studying the orthographic procedure first because it makes use of the familiar section and plan views, the latter including topographic, geologic, and structure contour maps, and so forth. Also, we believe that the use of the orthographic method gives a better initial three-dimensional perspective of the spacial relations involved in structural geology. Further, the nature of stereographic projection permits its use only with angular quantities (strike, dip, plunge, pitch, and the like); problems involving linear measures can only be solved completely by orthographic methods.

However, we do believe that once the student has learned to visualize in three dimensions, the study of the stereographic procedure becomes much easier. The solution of problems involving rotation, which is extremely difficult or impossible using orthographic procedures, is readily attainable by the stereographic method, which also permits more rapid solution of many other problems equally soluble by orthographic projection.

CHAPTER 8

Elements of Orthographic Projection

ORTHOGRAPHIC, OR NORMAL PROJECTION, is a method of representing a three-dimensional object on a two-dimensional surface. In order to give an accurate quantitative two-dimensional projection, each point in the object must be transferred (projected) to a desired plane along a line which is perpendicular to the plane. A plane so used is called the *plane of projection*.

In Figure 41 the point P at the center of the drawing is projected onto seven different planes along lines at right angles to these planes, giving projection points P_1 to P_7. The lines between P and the points of projection are called *projection lines*. Note that any number of projection planes are possible in addition to those illustrated. They may be in vertical or horizontal positions, as those shown, or they may be in inclined positions. For the most part in the applications to geology only horizontal and vertical planes of projection are involved.

Perspective drawings, useful in illustration, show distorted relationships, as was explained earlier in Chapter 1. We will therefore use two-dimensional drawings in all of our quantitative work. (A three-dimensional technique, known as *isometric projection*, permits the solution of some problems but is rarely used and will not be considered here.)

The technique of working with vertical planes involves the rotation of the vertical plane into the horizontal. Thus, any vertical plane of projection, such as those in Figure 41, could be rotated into the horizontal for purposes of quantitative work. The line about which the plane is rotated is called a *fold line*. This is illus-

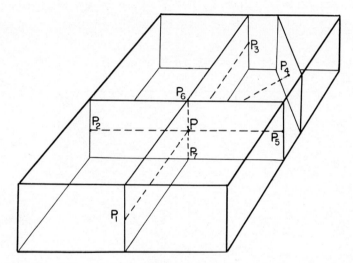

Fig. 41.   Diagram indicating orthographic projection of points.

trated in Figure 42. In Figure 42A, a line in space, *AB*, is projected onto a vertical plane *MNOR*, giving the projection A_1B_1, and onto a horizontal plane *ROPQ*, giving the projection A_2B_2. Figure 42B shows the vertical plane rotated about the fold line (*RO*) into a horizontal position. Note that A_1 and A_2 are different projections of the same point, *A*, and B_1 and B_2 are different projections of the point *B*. Line *CD* is projected in a similar manner onto the same vertical and horizontal planes, giving the projection C_1D_1 and C_2D_2.

Although perspective views will be used to help in the visualization and analysis of problems, all of the quantitative work will be done using different planes of projection which are rotated into the horizontal when necessary. Often more than one vertical plane will be involved in a problem, so that several fold lines may be used in a construction.

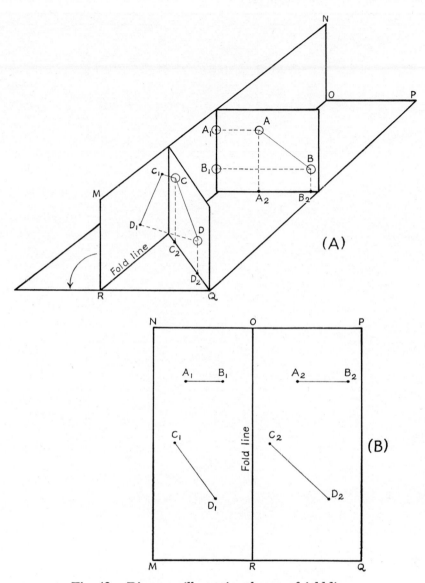

Fig. 42.   Diagrams illustrating the use of *fold lines*.

CHAPTER 9

Structure Contours

AN UNDERSTANDING OF structure contours is basic to the quantitative methods employed here, because most of the graphic solutions make use of them. Just as topographic contours are projections of lines of equal elevation of the ground surface onto a horizontal plane, so structure contours are projections onto a horizontal plane of lines of equal elevation on a given geologic horizon (usually a sedimentary bed). This is illustrated in Figure 43A where plane $MNOP$ is the surface of a dipping formation. The dashed lines are equal elevation lines drawn on the bed at intervals of 100 feet. These lines are then projected up to a horizontal plane. The projected lines are structure contours for the particular surface and are labeled for the appropriate elevations. Since the strike of a bed is defined as the direction of a horizontal line on a dipping bed, *all structure contours must be lines of strike.*

The structure contour map of this situation is shown in Figure 43B. Remember that structure contours are vertically above the actual depth lines they represent. Knowing this, it is possible to construct the actual dip of the formation from a structure contour map. In Figure 43C, a vertical plane beneath XY is rotated into the horizontal using X_1Y_1 as the fold line. The angle of dip can now be constructed in this plane. Draw elevation lines parallel to the horizontal fold line X_1Y_1, *using a vertical scale exactly equal to the horizontal scale.* By means of a procedure essentially the reverse of that used in obtaining the structure contours, we project from each contour to a level on a vertical plane having the same value as the contour. The line MP is obviously the dipping bed as it appears on a vertical plane perpendicular to the strike, and the angle PMY_1 is the angle of dip.

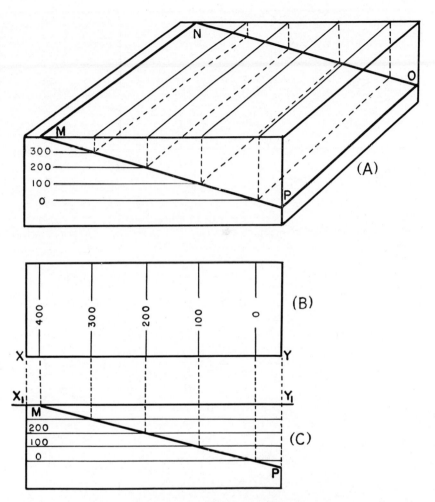

Fig. 43.   Diagrams explaining structure contours.

Structure contours reveal the type of structure that exists underground. Thus, a system of linear parallel contours, evenly spaced
and with progressively increasing values, indicates a simple homo-
clinal structure, that is, a structure dipping in one direction. Figure
43 illustrates such a case. Of course, differences in the angle of
dip are reflected in the spacing of the contour lines. This is exactly
analagous to topographic contours, where closely spaced contours
mean steep slopes and widely-spaced contours mean gentle slopes.

A fold with a horizontal axis is shown by parallel structure contours which have a sequence of values that are repeated symmetrically on each side of the axis. The values increase toward the axis of an anticline and decrease toward the axis of a syncline. In Figure 44 an asymmetric anticline is shown on the western part of the contour map. The axis of the anticline lies between the 1200-foot contour lines. The eastern portion of the map shows an asymmetric syncline plunging to the southwest.

The structure contour pattern for any bed in an uneroded fold (horizontal or plunging) resembles exactly the geologic outcrop pattern of a similar eroded fold. The block diagram in Figure 45A shows lines of equal elevation on a buried plunging anticline. These lines are projected to the surface as structure contours. The true structure contour map is illustrated in Figure 45B and shows a pattern similar to the geologic map of an eroded plunging anticline.

EXERCISES

1. Assume that the contours in Figure 44 are drawn for the top of a sandstone layer 200 feet thick and that the elevation of the ground surface is 2000 feet. Draw a reconstruction of the subsurface structure along the fold line AA'. (Keep vertical and horizontal scales equal.)

2. For the above problem, determine the average angles of dip for the limbs of each fold.

3. Sketch the structure contour map of the upper and lower surfaces of a sandstone layer dipping west. The sandstone lenses from maximum thickness at the east margin to zero thickness at the west margin. Use arbitrary values.

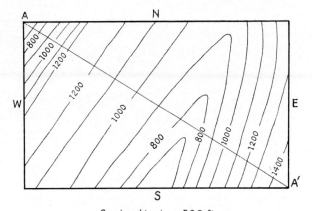

Scale : 1 inch = 500 ft.

Fig. 44.   Illustration of the asymmetry of folds by means of structure contours on a particular bed.

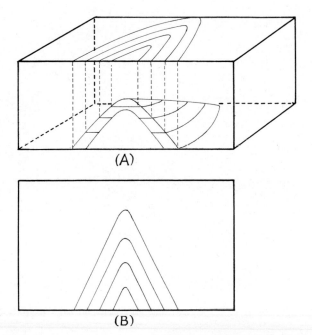

(A)

(B)

Fig. 45.   Structure contours on a plunging anticline: (A) block diagram;
(B) map view.

CHAPTER 10

True and Apparent Dip

Introduction

We have already noted that the angle of inclination of a dipping surface is at a maximum in a vertical plane taken perpendicular to the strike. When dip is given, it is always this maximum angle that is referred to. If both the direction and angle of dip are given, the strike is implicit, being at right angles to the dip direction.

Two methods of nomenclature are commonly used to express dip and strike in defining the attitude of a bed in space:

1. One method consists of giving the angle of dip followed by the direction of dip expressed as a bearing from north or south. Thus, 35° S 45 W means a dip of 35 degrees from the horizontal in a direction that is 45 degrees to the west of south. Since the dip direction is S 45 W, the strike must be N 45 W. The strike could also be given as S 45 E, but the first usage is more common. These relationships are shown in Figure 46.

2. A second and possibly more common method consists of stating the strike, followed by the angle and approximate direction of dip. With this nomenclature, only an approximate notation of dip direction is needed, because the true direction is perpendicular to the strike, which is stated precisely. The case shown above can then be described as N 45 W, 35° SW.

The angle of inclination of a bed on any vertical plane not perpendicular to the strike is a smaller angle than the true dip. This lesser angle is called the *apparent dip*. The apparent dip becomes progressively less and approaches zero as the vertical plane on which it is measured approaches the strike direction. This effect is shown in Figure 47, where the dip of a series of beds appears to vary from the maximum, true value on plane *1* (which is perpendicular to the strike), to zero on plane *4*, which is parallel to the strike.

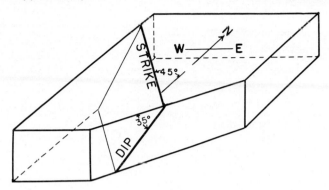

Fig. 46. Block diagram showing quantitative relationship between strike and dip.

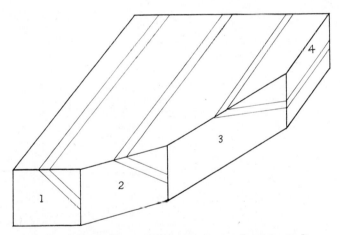

Fig. 47. Block diagram showing true and apparent dip.

The technique of orthographic projection provides a convenient and simple method for determining true dip when the apparent dip and the strike are known, or for determining the strike and true dip when two apparent dips are known.

True Dip from Strike and Apparent Dip

Example: Assume that a bed strikes east-west and has a certain apparent dip on a vertical plane which crosses the strike at a known acute angle. Determine the true dip.

In Figure 48A such a situation is analyzed, although in a distorted view. The bed *XYBC*, which has an east-west strike, has an apparent dip *AYB* in a plane which makes the known acute angle *XYA* with the strike. The true dip can be found only in a plane perpendicular to the strike, such as the north-south plane *MNOP*. The strike line *XY* is a structure contour line at zero depth. Any other line on the bed below the surface parallel to *XY* is also a strike line. Thus, from the arbitrary point *B* on the bed in the apparent dip plane, draw a line parallel to *XY*. This line then locates point *C*, on the dipping bed, in plane *MNOP*. Hence, angle *DXC* is the dip.

With this analysis in mind the true dip can easily be found by a simple graphic construction (refer to Figure 48B):

1. Draw the *strike line*.
2. Draw the fold line *FL1* in the direction of the apparent dip plane, intersecting the strike line at any point, such as *Y*.
3. Construct the apparent dip angle with vertex at *Y*. (Remember that this is drawn in a vertical plane rotated up to the horizontal about *FL1*.)
4. Draw an arbitrary structure contour parallel to the strike line. The intersection of the structure contour and *FL1* is designated here as point *A*. Point *B* is on the bed vertically below point *A*.
5. Draw *FL2* at right angles to the strike line at any point, such as *X*. Point *D* is established where *FL2* intersects the structure contour.
6. Since *AD* is the structure contour for the depth *AB*, point *C* may be located in the north-south vertical plane by dropping vertically from *D* to a depth equal to *AB*.
7. Connect *X* and *C*. The angle *DXC* is the true dip.

The construction lines in Figure 48B are analagous to those in Figure 48A. Note that the procedure in stages 6 and 7 involves merely the construction of the angle of dip when two or more structure contours are given, as explained in connection with Figure 43.

If the strike and true dip were given it is obvious that the apparent dip could be determined by following the same procedure outlined above but starting with the plane of the true dip.

True Dip and Strike from Two Apparent Dips

It may be necessary to determine the strike and true dip from two apparent dips of the same bed found through either surface observations or subsurface drilling. The procedure consists of find-

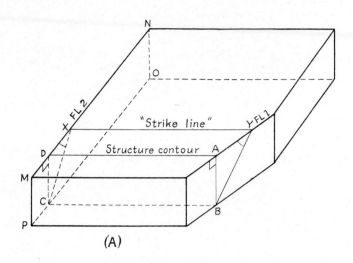

(A)

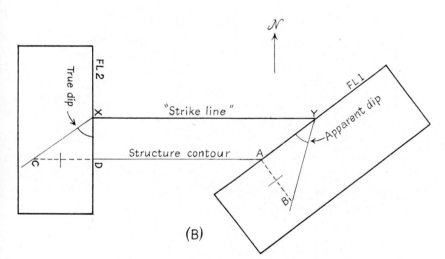

(B)

Fig. 48.   Solution of true dip from strike and apparent dip.

ing two structure contours on a particular bed. The strike is then the bearing of either contour, and the dip is found by projecting the contours onto a vertical plane normal to them, as given above.

Example: On a vertical cliff trending N 60 E, the apparent dip of a bed is 26° NE; on a second cliff which trends N 10 E, the same bed dips at 19° SW. Find the strike and true dip of the bed.

Assume that the two cliffs or vertical planes intersect each other. This permits the finding of structure contours on a specific bed (refer to Figure 49).

1. Consider the cliff lines as fold lines, such as *FL*1 and *FL*2.
2. Draw the two apparent dip angles, starting at the point of intersection. (They may be drawn on either side of the fold line, whichever is most convenient for the construction.)
3. From an arbitrary point *A* on *FL*1 drop a vertical (of depth *h*) to the bed. Find the position of an equal vertical beneath *FL*2 thus locating point *B*. *A* and *B* are thus points on the surface projected from equal depths on the same bed and therefore lie on a structure contour representing *h* depth. A line parallel to this contour passing through the intersection of the two fold lines (which are surface lines) is therefore a contour at zero depth, or at the surface. The strike of either of these lines, measured from the north, is found to be N 30 E and gives the strike of the bed.

To find the dip, draw *FL*3 normal to the strike. Following the procedure for obtaining dip from two or more structure contours, the true dip is found to be 45 degrees.

Figure 50 is a three-dimensional analysis of the situation and indicates part of the solution.

EXERCISES

1. A bed strikes N 70 W and shows a dip of 45° SE on a vertical plane that trends N 55 W. Find the true dip.
2. A vein has a known strike and dip of N 55 E 60° NW. Find the apparent dip on two drift faces which trend north-south and east-west in an underground mine.
3. A vein shows a dip of 34° SW on the face of a mine drift oriented N 35 E. The same vein shows a dip of 12° SW on the face of a drift oriented N 10 E. Find the angle and direction of the apparent dip of this vein on a tunnel planned to trend N 45 W.
4. The angle of apparent dip of an underground bed determined from two drill holes in a north-south line is 38° S. From two drill holes in an east-west line, the apparent dip of the bed is 55° E. Find the strike and true dip of the bed.

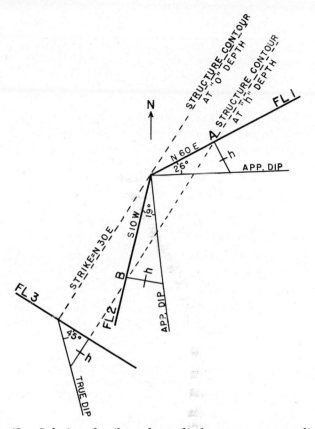

Fig. 49.   Solution of strike and true dip from two apparent dips.

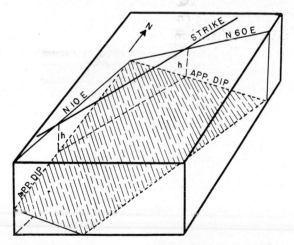

Fig. 50.   Three-dimensional analysis of solution in Figure 49.

CHAPTER 11

Dip and Strike from Three Points

Three Points, Two at Same Elevation

The basic problem in strike determination is to establish a structure contour for some elevation on a bed. If two points are known to be at the same elevation the line of strike is obtained immediately by connecting the two points with a structure contour. A second structure contour (parallel to the first) can be drawn through a known third point, which is at a different elevation. The dip is then found by construction in a plane perpendicular to the strike.

Example: Figure 51 shows a topographic map and the location of three points on the top of a given bed. Find the strike and dip of this bed.

Points *A* and *C* lie on the same topographic contour—2000 feet. The line connecting *A* and *C*, and extended to the edges of the map, is the 2000-foot structure contour which shows the strike to be N 90 E or east-west. Where broken, this contour is on that part of the bed that has actually been removed by erosion. Point *B* locates an outcrop of the same surface at an elevation of 1800 feet. A line through *B* parallel to *AC* is thus the 1800-foot structure contour. The true dip, which can be constructed in any vertical plane normal to the strike, is drawn just off the map, using *FL1* as the top line of the section. (Remember that the scale used in the vertical plane must equal the horizontal map scale.) The graphic solution gives a dip angle of 31° S.

Three Points at Different Elevations

Commonly, subsurface drill-core data yield random elevations for a given bed. In such cases, a minimum of three elevation values is necessary to work out the strike and dip. The problem is once again reduced to the determination of a structure contour line on the bed. This is accomplished by locating a fourth point whose elevation is equivalent to one of the three known elevations. In the solution of this generalized three-point problem the strike can be obtained by any one of three procedures given below. The construction for dip determination is the same in all cases and was given in connection with Figure 43.

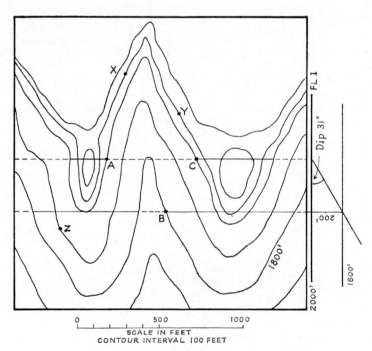

Fig. 51.   Determination of strike and dip from three points with two at the same elevation.

Example: Three drill holes—*A*, *B*, and *C*—starting from a level surface encounter a dipping coal seam. Hole *B* is 1000 feet S 50 E of hole *A*, and hole *C* is 1200 feet S 30 W of hole *A*. The depths of the coal seam beneath each hole are as follows: *A*—600 feet, *B*—900 feet, *C*—1600 feet. Find the strike and dip of the coal seam.

Procedure 1: Method of Two Apparent Dips. In Figure 52, points *A*, *B*, and *C*, which are the locations of the drill holes, can also be considered as projections to the horizontal of the three points on the seam which have the given depths. Clearly, the seam must be dipping in the general direction from *A* to *C*, as *A* is the shallowest and *C* the deepest of the holes.

Starting with the shallowest point *A* (the highest given point on the bed), two apparent dips can be constructed in the vertical planes beneath fold lines *FL1* and *FL2*. The apparent dip angles are BAB_1 and CAC_1, respectively. Note that the depth BB_1 is 300 feet, not 900 feet, for the seam is only 300 feet deeper at *B* than at *A*. Similarly *C* is 1000 feet deeper than *A*, so that the depth CC_1 is 1000 feet. The same horizontal and vertical scale must be used.

Now let us find, by trial and error, a point *P* on line *FL2* such that the depth PP_1 equals depth BB_1, or 300 feet. The line *BP* is a structure contour and establishes the strike. Structure contours, shown by the broken lines, can be drawn through points *A* and *C*, parallel to the established strike. The true dip is found in the vertical section below *FL3*, taken normal to the strike, and is constructed as shown.

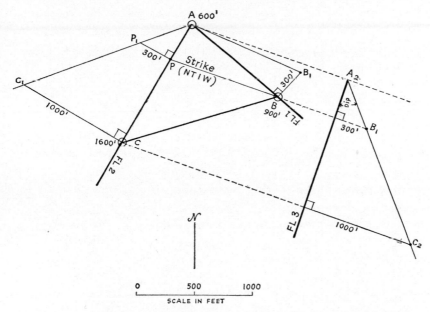

Fig. 52.   Solution of the three-point problem using two apparent dips.

Procedure 2: Alternate Projection Method. This problem can also be solved by a simple projection procedure. In Figure 53, points A, B, and C represent the surface locations of the three drill holes described above. Again, consider these points to be the projections onto the horizontal of the three points on the bed. The points on the dipping bed can also be projected onto any vertical plane, such as the arbitrary plane rotated into the horizontal about $FL1$. The points A_1, B_1, and C_1 are the projections on this vertical plane of the three points on the inclined bed.

To find points A_1, B_1, and C_1, simply draw lines from A, B, and C perpendicular to the fold line used and descend to the appropriate depths below the fold line. Any horizontal line or contour on the bed will also appear as a horizontal line when projected to this vertical plane. Thus, the horizontal line drawn through B_1 is the projection of a line on the bed at the depth of B_1, or 900 feet. P_1 is located where the horizontal crosses line A_1C_1 on the vertical section. P_1 is therefore the projection to the vertical section of a point on the 900-foot depth line where this crosses a line on the bed directly beneath AC.

To find this point on the horizontal plane, draw a line from P_1 perpendicular to the fold line until it cuts line AC. Point P, located at this intersection, is the projection to the horizontal of a point on the bed at a depth of 900 feet. Line BP is therefore a 900-foot depth structure contour and establishes the strike. It should be realized that any horizontal line drawn on the vertical section can be transferred to the horizontal plane to give a different structure contour. Also the fold line can have any orientation, and the same strike would be obtained. Once the strike is found by this procedure, the dip is determined in a vertical section perpendicular to the strike.

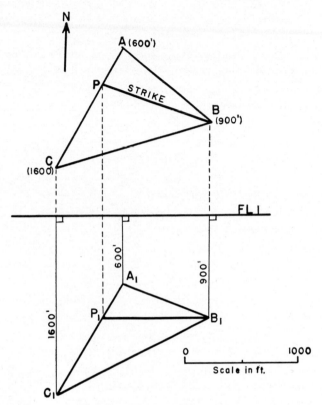

Fig. 53.   Solution of the three-point problem using a variation of the projection method.

A three-dimensional analysis of such a problem is shown in Figure 54, where the dipping bed is represented by the plane $STUV$ and the three points on this plane are circled at A_2, B_2, and C_2. Points A, B, and C are projections of these onto the horizontal, and A_1, B_1, and C_1 are projections onto the vertical section. (The vertical section passes through point C_2 on the bed, so that C_1 and C_2 are identical.) If this vertical section is rotated to the horizontal about $FL1$, then the top view and this rotated section will be similar to Figure 53. P_2 is a point on the bed at depth B_2 and also lies on a line (not drawn) connecting A_2 with C_2 on the bed. The solution involved the location of point P at the surface. The horizontal B_1P_1 on the vertical section is a projection of the horizontal passing through B_2P_2 on the bed. From the information on the vertical view, we can find P on the horizontal as shown in Figure 53.

Procedure 3: Geometric Methods. The strike can also be determined by two simple geometric methods when three points at different depths on a bed are known. In Figure 55, points A, B, and C again represent the surface locations of the three drill holes. Point A represents the highest point of the three, and C the lowest. Somewhere along the line AC there must be a point that represents the projection of a point on the bed having the same depth as B. By finding this point the strike can be obtained.

The geometric construction for both solutions is based on the proposition from plane geometry, "corresponding parts of similar triangles are in proportion." It is convenient to work with the difference in depth between the drill holes rather than the actual depths. Starting with the point A (the highest point), draw line AF at an arbitrary length and direction. It is best to draw this line roughly in the direction of the deepest hole, although almost any direction may be used. Divide line AF into a number of equal parts, using an arbitrary but convenient scale. Point C_1 is located along line AF at a distance which is proportional to the difference in depth between holes A and C. (Each division on AF is proportional to 100 feet in this case.) The depth equivalent to that of hole B along AF is marked at P_1. Draw line CC_1. Then draw a line from P_1 parallel to CC_1 until this line cuts AC, thus locating point P. Since point C represents the surface projection of the depth scaled off at AC_1, point P must represent the surface projection of the depth scaled off at AP_1, which is also the depth at B. The line BP is a structure contour for the depth of 900 feet and establishes the strike.

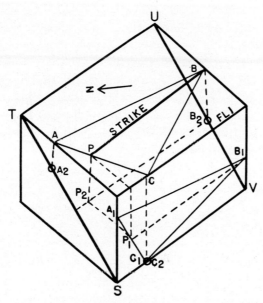

Fig. 54.   Three-dimensional analysis of the three-point problem as given in
Figure 53.

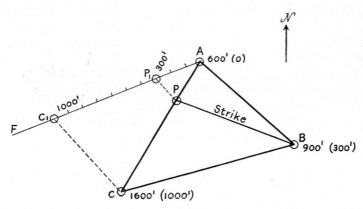

Fig. 55.   Solution of the three-point problem by a geometric method.

A second method, based on similar geometric reasoning, requires very little construction. The three surface-hole locations are once again shown in Figure 56, together with the differences in depth between points on the bed beneath A and C and beneath A and B. Note again that somewhere along line AC there must be a point (P) which is the projection of a point on the bed having the same depth as that at B. We can deduce at a glance that the closer the depth of hole B is to A, the nearer to A will point P lie. Remembering the construction and solution just given in Figure 55, we can set up the following relationship:

$$\frac{\text{Difference in depth from } A \text{ to } C}{\text{Difference in depth from } A \text{ to } B} = \frac{\text{Distance } AC}{\text{Distance } AP}$$

We know all values in this equation except AP. Substituting actual values in the equation we have:

$$\frac{1000}{300} = \frac{1200}{AP} \text{ and } AP = 3/10 \, (1200)$$

After AP is measured off as 3/10 of line AC, draw BP and thus establish the strike.

EXERCISES

1. Points X, Y, and Z in Figure 51 are outcrops of the same surface of a dike which cuts the structure. Find the strike and dip of this dike.

2. Three drill holes, starting from the same elevation, encounter the top of a coal seam at these depths: hole 1—2100 feet, hole 2—1200 feet, hole 3—1000 feet. Hole 2 is located 3000 feet S 70 E of hole 1, and hole 3 is located 3400 feet S 10 E of hole 1. Find the strike and dip of the seam by the four procedures described.

3. Find the strike and dip of a marker horizon from the following field data:

Hole	Elevation of ground surface	Depth of horizon	Location
A	4200 ft.	800 ft.	
B	6000 ft.	2000 ft.	4800 ft. N45E of A
C	5100 ft.	2100 ft.	3500 ft. N15W of A

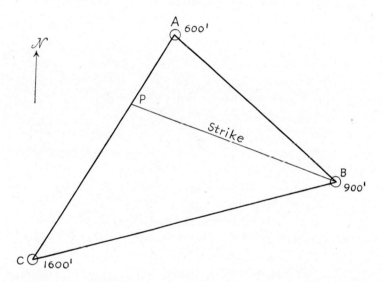

Fig. 56.   Solution of the three-point problem by a second geometric
procedure.

CHAPTER 12

Strike and Dip from Drill-Core Data

Introduction

We have seen in Chapter 11 that the depth data from three vertical drill holes to some marker horizon permit the determination of strike and dip. If only two vertical drill cores with known depths to a marker horizon are available, the true angle of dip and two possible strike directions (one in a special case) are obtainable. If no marker horizon is recognizable the strike cannot be determined from vertical drill cores by graphic means, because the rotating drill stem destroys the orientation. However, the angle of dip can always be measured from the relation of the bedding to the drill core. If core data is available from an inclined drill hole as well as from a vertical hole, the angle of dip and a limited number of strike directions can be determined (one in special cases) without the presence of a marker horizon. The techniques discussed in this chapter apply to uniform dip and strike.

Vertical Drill Holes

A specific problem, which is solved below, illustrates the general procedures that can be used in the solution of cases where core and depth data are available from only two vertical holes.

Example: Two drill holes lie on an east-west line 2500 feet apart (see Figure 57). The western hole *A* reaches a given bed at 800 feet. Hole *B*, to the east, reaches the same layer at 2000 feet. This is shown in the vertical section below *FL*1. The bedding makes an angle of 40 degrees with the axis of the hole (core-bedding angle). Find the possibilities of strike and dip.

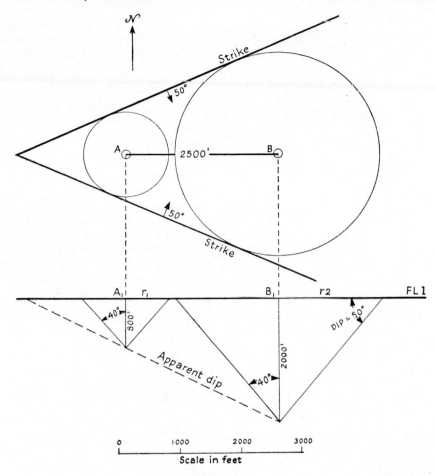

Fig. 57. Solution for strike and dip using vertical drill-core data—the general case.

For vertical cores, the core-bedding angle is the complement of the dip and is called the *hade*. Thus, the angle of dip is 50 degrees, but the direction of dip is not directly measurable.

From the bottom of each drill hole extend lines to the surface at angles of 40 degrees with the hole axis. This construction about each hole can be considered a section through a cone, whose sides make an angle of 40 degrees with the conic axis. Thus the actual direction of dip must be included somewhere on the sides of each of these cones. Each hole considered separately gives an infinite number of possible dip directions. However, if both holes are considered, these possibilities can be reduced by finding the plane(s) which include(s) an element from each cone, as shown below.

The intersection of these cones with the surface produces the two circles shown in Figure 57. These circles are drawn about A and B, using r_1 and r_2 as radii. Each circle represents the locus of outcrops of beds that dip at 50 degrees and reach the bottom of each hole at the given depth. The infinity of tangents to each circle represents an infinity of strike directions associated with each possible dip direction.

How many strike directions are there which if associated with a 50-degree dip will reach the bottom of each hole at the given depth? Only those strikes represented by external tangents common to both circles satisfy this condition. The two possible strikes for this problem are labeled in Figure 57. Dip directions are shown by arrows. Note that the two strike possibilities intersect in a point where the bed should outcrop. If only this point were desired, it could be found by extending the straight line joining the bottom of each hole to the surface. Clearly, this line gives the apparent dip of the bed in an east-west section.

Figure 58 shows the special case in which the drill holes are on a line oriented exactly normal to the strike, or in the direction of dip. Note that only one possible tangent common to both circles exists, and this gives the strike uniquely. Note also that in the vertical section, the apparent dip, as given by the line joining the bottom of both holes, coincides with the true dip as shown by the conic construction.

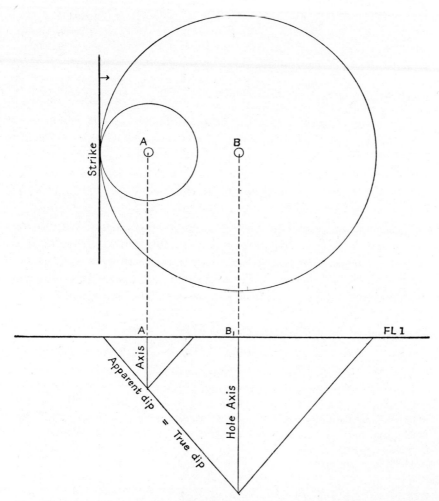

Fig. 58.   Special case of vertical drill-core data where holes are on line normal to strike.

In Figure 59 the two drill holes lie on a line parallel to the strike. The construction results in a unique strike direction, since both tangents are parallel to each other, but yields two possible dip directions. Note also that the fact that both holes encounter the bed at the same depth indicates that the holes lie along the strike.

Inclined Drill Holes

If no marker horizon is present and data from one vertical and one inclined hole are available, dip and strike possibilities are obtainable in much the same manner as in the preceding section. Direct measurements of the angle between the bedding and the axis of the vertical hole give the hade. In general two variable relationships can exist between the inclined hole and the bedding: (1) the inclined hole can be gentler or steeper than the angle of dip of the beds; (2) the direction of inclination of the hole can vary with respect to the strike. Variations in these relationships determine the number of strike and dip possibilities obtainable in this procedure. These possibilities may vary from one to four.

Inclination of Hole Less than Dip of Beds

The procedure for getting dip and strike directions is explained for a general case of four possibilities of strike.

Example: The angle between bedding and axis of a vertical hole *A* is 20 degrees. (The depth of the hole is unimportant, since no marker is encountered.) Five hundred feet N 30 E of hole *A*, hole *B* is drilled and is inclined due west at an angle of 50 degrees with the horizontal. The bedding makes an angle of 15 degrees with the axis of the inclined hole. What are the strike and dip possibilities?

The angle of dip is obviously 70 degrees (the complement of the hade). Clearly the information obtained from the vertical drill core is the same as would be obtained from any vertical drill core in this area. Since no marker horizon exists, we can imagine the vertical hole as being located in such a position that it will intersect the inclined hole at an arbitrary but convenient depth. The hypothetical intersection of these holes must occur at one point in a particular bed. The imaginary vertical hole must lie in the vertical plane which includes the inclined hole, otherwise the two will not meet. The horizontal distance between holes is unimportant, since we can imagine the vertical hole placed anywhere.

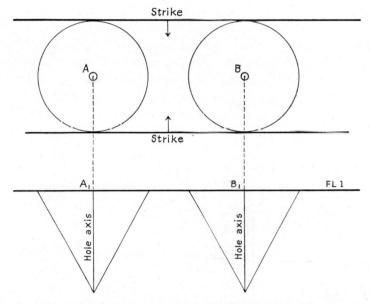

Fig. 59. Special case of vertical drill-core data where holes are on line parallel to the strike.

Place hole A due west of hole B, so that an east-west vertical section will include both holes (see Figure 60). The two holes intersect at point P in the vertical section below $FL1$. From point P draw lines making angles of 20 degrees and 15 degrees, respectively, with the axes of A_1 and B_1. These lines represent possible positions of the bed as seen in this section. Again the cone about each axis represents all possible bed positions for each core. If both holes are considered, we can again limit possibilities. The circle about A represents the locus of all outcrops from which a bed can dip at 70 degrees and reach point P. The cone about the inclined hole clearly intersects the surface in an ellipse, as drawn about B. (See the appendix for a method of constructing an ellipse.) This ellipse is the locus of all outcrops from which beds can dip at 70 degrees and reach point P while making at the same time an angle of 15 degrees with the axis of the inclined hole.

Only tangents common to both circle and ellipse can be considered as strike possibilities. In this most general case four exist, as shown in Figure 60.

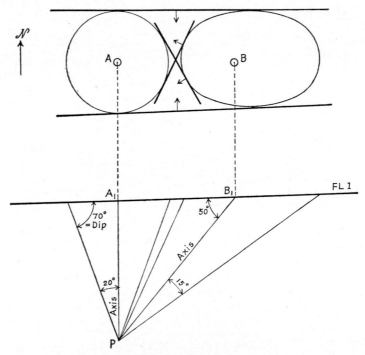

Fig. 60.   Solution for strike and dip using core data from one vertical and one inclined hole—a general case.

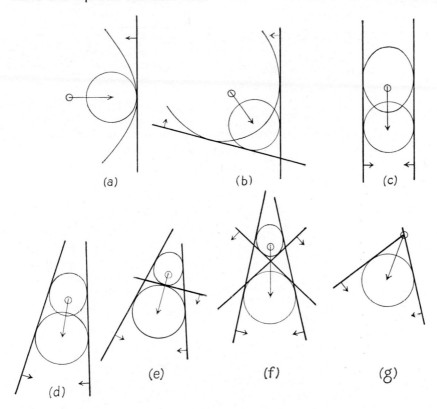

Fig. 61.   Various solutions for strike and dip using core data from one vertical and one inclined hole where inclination of the inclined hole is less than the dip of the beds. The long arrow is the horizontal component of the inclined hole and shows direction of inclination. The short arrows show possible dip directions. (Modified from Mead)

In more special cases the possibility exists of obtaining three, two, or one strike (and dip) direction(s). These cases depend upon the relation between direction of the inclined hole and the strike of the beds. The general procedure outlined above will solve any of these cases. The various possibilities are given in Figure 61. In this figure the long arrow is the horizontal projection of the inclined drill hole from the surface to the point of intersection with the vertical drill hole. Note that F is similar to the general case solved above. The relatively small size of the ellipse here occurs because the angle between the beds and the core axis is very small for the case selected. Note that in A a parabola, rather than an ellipse, results.

Inclination of Hole Steeper than Dip of Beds

When this relation exists, the circle and ellipse resulting from the construction either intersect each other or lie internally tangent to each other. In the former case two strike and dip possibilities exist, and in the latter the solution is unique. The possibilities that can exist with different relations between strike of beds and direction of hole inclination are shown in Figure 62. The general construction procedure given above will again give specific solutions to any problem of this type.

EXERCISES

1. Draw the internal tangents in Figure 57. Why can't these be possible strike directions?

2. Drill hole A encounters a marker horizon at a depth of 400 feet. Drill hole B located 2000 feet N 30 W of A encounters the same marker at a depth of 1000 feet. The angle between the hole axis and the bedding is 33 degrees. The flat bedrock surface is covered by 100 feet of overburden. Where would you locate a drill hole to test the marker horizon at the base of the overburden? What is the amount of dip, and what are the possible directions of dip and strike?

3. In an area of sedimentary rocks known to have a uniform dip, two diamond drill holes are made on an east-west line, 200 feet apart. No horizon marker is found in the examination of the cores.

Hole *1:* vertical; beds make an angle of 20 degrees with the axis of the hole.

Hole *2:* 200 feet west of hole *1;* inclined N 45 E at an angle of 50 degrees with the horizontal; beds make an angle of 15 degrees with the axis of the hole.

What are the dip and strike possibilities?

4. What are dip and strike possibilities for beds for which the following core information is obtained?

Hole *A:* vertical; beds make an angle of 60 degrees with the axis of the hole.

Hole *B:* 300 feet N 45 W of hole *A;* inclined due west at an angle of 70 degrees to the horizontal; beds make an angle of 80 degrees with the axis of the hole.

5. The axis of a vertical drill hole makes an angle of 20 degrees with sedimentary beds. One hundred feet to the north of this vertical hole, a drill hole inclined 54 degrees to the horizontal in a direction N 30 E shows the beds parallel to the axis of the hole. What is the angle and direction(s) of dip? What are the strike possibilities?

6. The angle between the bedding and the axis of the core taken from a vertical hole is 25 degrees. West of the vertical hole, at a distance of 200 feet, is a drill hole inclined due west at an angle of 55 degrees with the horizontal. The beds make an angle of 10 degrees with the axis of this hole. What are the dip and strike possibilities?

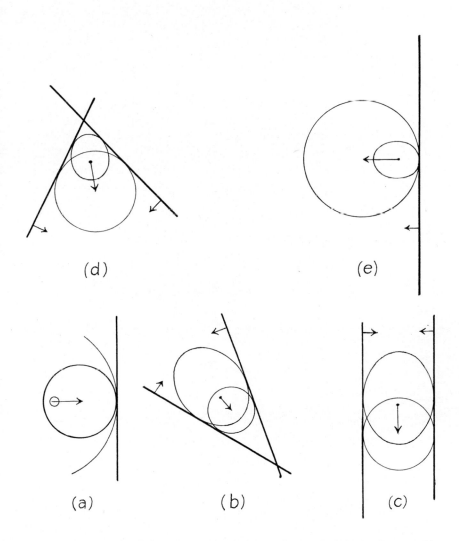

(d)

(e)

(a)

(b)

(c)

Fig. 62. Inclined drill-core solutions where the inclination of the inclined hole is greater than the dip of the beds. (Modified from Mead)

CHAPTER 13

Thickness and Depth of Strata

IT IS FREQUENTLY NECESSARY to calculate the depth to a given bed or to determine its thickness if the width of outcrop and angle of dip are known. Figure 63 illustrates the relationship between width of outcrop *AB;* thickness *CD;* angle of dip *EAG;* depth to the top of the bed *EF,* at point *E;* depth to the bottom of the bed *EG;* and apparent thickness as shown by a vertical drill hole *FG.* If the strike and dip of a bed are known, its depth from any point on the surface and the quantitative relationship between thickness and width of outcrop can be obtained by a simple graphic procedure which involves only the drawing of data to scale. The desired information can then be taken directly from the graph.

Example: Figure 64 shows a common situation where a dipping layer outcrops on a flat surface. Point *A* lies on the bottom, and point *B* on the top of a bed which is known to have a dip of 30° E and a strike north-south. Determine the depths to the top and bottom of the bed at point *P* and the thickness of the bed.

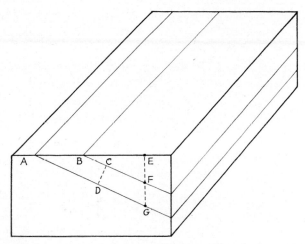

Fig. 63.   Diagram showing the relationship between width of outcrop (A, B), thickness of bed (C, D), and apparent thickness (F, G).

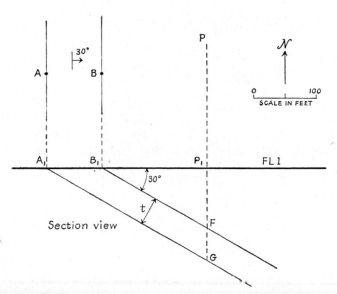

Fig. 64.   Solution for thickness of, and depth to, a given bed when width of outcrop and strike and dip are known, and ground surface is horizontal.

The solution involves drawing a vertical section at right angles to the strike. The scale of this section must be the same as that of the map. Such a section shows the true dip. The map locations A, B, and P, when projected onto the vertical section, are represented by A_1, B_1 and P_1. The bottom and top lines of the bed are drawn through points A_1 and B_1, respectively, at the proper dip. The thickness t can be measured directly, using the same scale as the map scale. The distance P_1F is the desired depth to the top of the bed, and P_1G is the depth to the bottom of the bed.

Example: Assume a situation similar to that above with the exception that the ground surface is not level but slopes at an angle of 10 degrees in the same direction as the dip in the bed.

The solution for the same quantities is shown in Figure 65, where the desired values can be taken directly from the section and converted to proper dimensions, using the scale. Note that points A and B are projections to the horizontal of points A_1 and B_1, whose separation is the width of outcrop on the ground surface.

Example: Assume a situation similar to the first example above, with the exception in this case that the ground slopes at an angle of 15 degrees in a direction opposite to the dip of the bed.

The solution is given in Figure 66.

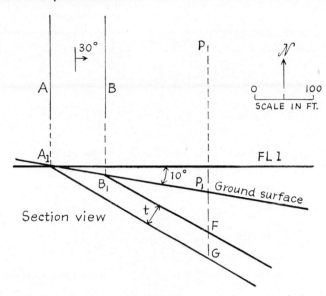

Fig. 65. Similar solution to that of Figure 64, but ground slopes in same direction as bed.

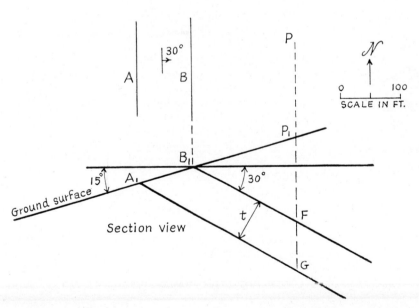

Fig. 66. Similar solution to that of Fig. 64, but ground slopes opposite to dip beds.

Example: Point *A* on the bottom of a bed which strikes N 10 W and dips 30° E is located at an elevation of 1000 feet. Point *B* on the top of the same bed lies 600 feet N 50 E of point *A* and is at an elevation of 900 feet. What is the thickness of the bed, and what is its depth at point *P*, which is at an elevation of 1450 feet and lies 1000 feet due east of point *A*?

In Figure 67, Points *A*, *B*, and *P* are located, using a convenient scale. The line of strike through A marks the bottom of the bed at the 1000-foot elevation, and the line of strike drawn through *B* marks the top of the bed at the 900-foot elevation. The three points are then projected onto a vertical section drawn at right angles to the strike. Points A_1, B_1, and P_1 are the three points projected onto this vertical plane. Lines drawn through A_1 and B_1 at angles of 30 degrees from *FL*1 mark the bottom and top of the bed, respectively. The thickness (t) of the bed can be scaled off directly. The depth of the top of the bed below point *P* is the distance P_1P_2, measured at right angles to *FL*1.

EXERCISES

1. A bed dips at an angle of 35 degrees. The surface of the ground is level, and the distance between the upper and lower contacts of the bed measured at right angles to the strike is 200 feet. Find the thickness of the bed.

2. Find the thickness of a bed if the width of outcrop between upper and lower contacts is 150 feet as measured at right angles to the strike. The ground surface slopes 20° E, and the bed dips 45° E.

3. Assume the same conditions as in the problem 2, but with the change that the ground slopes 20 degrees in a direction opposite to the dip. Find the thickness of the bed.

4. A point on the bottom of a bed which strikes east-west is at an elevation of 1200 feet. At a distance of 700 feet S 30 W of this point is an outcrop of the top of the bed. The elevation here is 1500 feet. If the bed dips 25° S, find the true thickness and, also, the apparent thickness as would be revealed in a vertical drill hole.

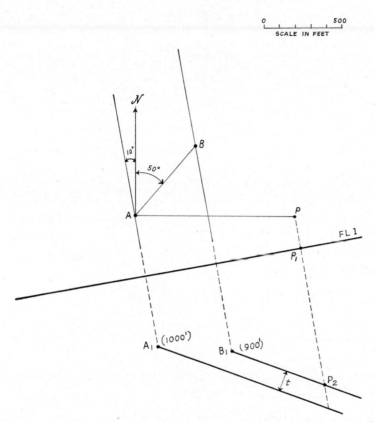

Fig. 67.   General solution for thickness of, and depth to, a given bed when the apparent width of outcrop (A, B) is known and where the ground surface is not level.

CHAPTER 14

Completion of Areal Outcrop Patterns

WHENEVER THE ATTITUDE OF layered rocks is known or can be determined, the areal outcrop pattern can be drawn by graphic procedures on an available topographic map of the area. This procedure is useful when the bedrock is mostly covered or when parts of the area are inaccessible. It must be assumed that the attitude and the thickness of formations is uniform over the given area.

It was noted in Chapter 2 that the contacts between horizontal rock units must be parallel to topographic contours. Thus, if thickness or contacts are known for one locality, the entire outcrop pattern can be drawn by simply extrapolating the contacts parallel to contours. On the other hand, if beds are vertical, the contacts will always be straight lines trending across country, regardless of topography. The problem requires graphic construction when the beds are inclined at some angle other than 90 degrees. This procedure can also be applied to folded rocks by considering each flank to be simply a sequence of tilted beds.

Example: An example of the procedure to be used is given in Figure 68, which is a topographic map of an eroded area. Points *A, B,* and *C* show the outcrop position of three points on the top of a sandstone bed 100 feet thick. Find the strike and dip of the sandstone bed and complete its outcrop pattern, or areal distribution.

1. Number the contour lines, using the bench mark (2150 feet) as reference.

2. Connect points *A* and *C,* which are both on the 1800-foot contour line. This is a structure contour for the upper surface of the bed and, hence, is a line of strike (east-west).

3. Draw a vertical section normal to the strike below *FL1* and draw levels corresponding to the surface contour lines, using the same scale as the map scale.

100

4. Project A, C, and B to the appropriate levels at points A_1, C_1, and B_1. Note that points A_1 and C_1 are identical. The line connecting these points gives the dip of the top of the bed ($24°$ S).

5. Making use of this section, we can project structure contours on the map for the top of the sandstone layer. The contours are drawn solidly where they lie beneath present topography, and broken where the rock has actually been eroded. Only at points where structure contours cross topographic contours of the same value do actual exposures of the top of the sandstone bed occur.

6. Connect all such crossing points with a continuous line. This line represents the areal outcrop of the top of the sandstone layer.

7. On the section, draw the bottom of the bed parallel to the top, at a distance equivalent to a thickness of 100 feet. (Note that thickness is measured along a line normal to the top and bottom surfaces and not a vertical line.)

8. Draw structure contours for the bottom of the bed and, using the same procedure as for the top, mark points where the structure contours cross the same topographic contours. These points are marked on the illustration, but the structure contours on the bottom of the bed are omitted so as not to complicate the drawing.

9. Connect these points with a continuous line, which marks the outcrop of the bottom of the bed.

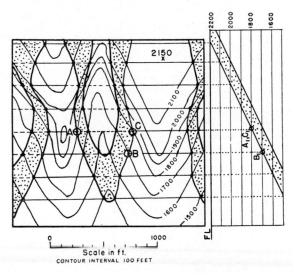

Fig. 68.   Procedure for the completion of areal outcrop pattern when strike, dip, and topography are given.

CHAPTER 15

Intersecting Surfaces; Plunge and Pitch; Lineation

The geologist must frequently describe the position in space taken by a subsurface line. This may be the line of intersection or *trace* of two planar structures, such as the trace of (1) a fault with a dike, sedimentary bed, or other layered structure; (2) the axial plane of a fold with bedding surfaces; (3) cleavage with bedding; or (4) veins with faults. Further, the subsurface lines may be slickensides on a fault surface or some form of lineation.

The orientation of any such line is usually given by the compass direction of its horizontal projection (azimuth or bearing) and its plunge. If the orientation with respect to a dipping plane is desired, then the pitch of the line in that plane is given. Remember that plunge is an angle measured in the vertical plane between the horizontal and an inclined line, and pitch is the angle between the horizontal and an inclined line measured in a dipping plane which includes the line. These terms were used earlier to describe fold axes.

Example: A rich ore zone occurs where a vein crosses a standstone bed, both of which outcrop at the surface. The vein strikes N 40 E and dips 60° SE; the bed strikes N 50 W and has a dip of 40° SW. Find (1) the angle and direction of plunge of the ore zone; (2) the surface location of a vertical shaft to meet the ore zone at a depth of 300 feet; (3) the total length of the ore zone if it runs out below the 500-foot depth; (4) the pitch of the ore zone measured on the vein; and (5) the shortest distance (for an inclined shaft) from the outcrop of the vein to the ore body at the 300-foot depth.

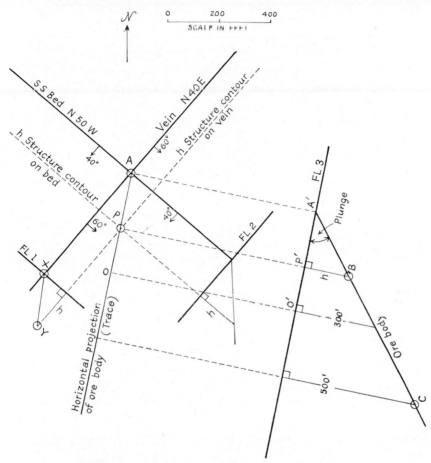

Fig. 69A.   Solution involving intersecting surfaces.

The ore zone can be considered as the zone of intersection of the vein and bed. In the procedure which follows, we will work only with the upper surfaces of these dipping structures.

1. Draw the surface outcrops of vein and bed, as in Figure 69A.

2. Draw structure contours for an arbitrary depth h for both vein and bed.

3. The intersection of the surface outcrops of vein and bed locates one point (A) on the ore body. The point of intersection P of the two structure contours locates the horizontal projection of a second point on the ore body, at h depth. Line AP, continued southward, thus represents the surface projection of the ore body, or trace of the vein and bed on each other.

4. The direction of plunge of the ore body is simply the bearing of the line *AP* from point A.

5. The angle of plunge must be found in the vertical plane including *AP*. For simplicity in the diagram we will use *A′P′* as the fold line *FL*3, parallel to the line *AP*. On the vertical section below *FL*3, draw *P′B* equal to depth *h*. Thus *A′B* and its continuation represents the true inclination of the ore body, and angle *P′A′B* is the angle of plunge.

6. Find where a depth of 300 feet meets the ore body below *FL*3. Project this depth to the surface at *O′* and thus *O* on the continuation of AP is the desired surface location of a vertical shaft to meet the ore body at a depth of 300 feet.

7. Locate a point *C* on the ore body 500 feet vertically below *FL*3. The length *A′C* is the total length of the ore body.

8. The angle measured on the vein between the surface outcrop of the vein and the ore zone is the desired angle of pitch. The angle *OAX* is thus the projection of the pitch angle. In order to measure the true pitch, which lies in the inclined plane of the vein, we must rotate the vein to the surface about line *AX*. For simplicity in illustration this construction is given in Figure 69B.

a. Lay off *XZ* parallel to fold line *FL*1 and equal to *XY*. This is equivalent to rotating *XY* to the surface.

b. Draw *ZS* parallel to *AX*. The figure *XZSR* thus represents a portion of the vein down to the depth *h* rotated to the surface about *AX*, and line *ZS* represents the actual contour at this depth.

c. We must find the trace of the ore body (of which *AP* is the horizontal projection) on the rotated surface. Remember that *Y′* and *P* are surface projections from the same depth *h*. As point *Y* at this depth appears at *Z* after rotation to the surface, the point for which *P* is the projection must, by analogy, appear at *P′*.

d. As line *AP′* represents the actual ore zone on the rotated vein, the angle *XAP′* must be the pitch.

e. The perpendicular distance from line *AX* to *O′* is the shortest distance to the ore body at the 300-foot level, measured from the outcrop of the vein.

EXERCISES

1. A fault strikes N 50 E and dips 70° SE. A vein strikes N 60 W and dips 30° NE. Find the direction and angle of plunge of the line of inter-

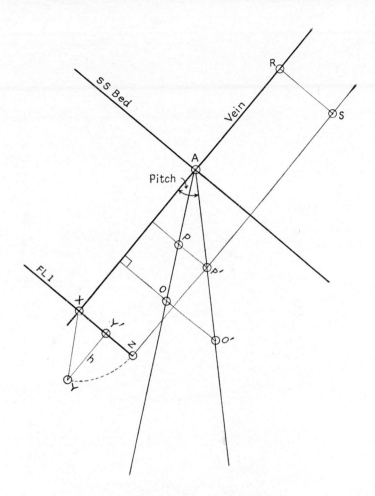

Fig. 69B.   Solution involving intersecting surfaces.

section of the two structures. What is the shortest distance to run an inclined shaft down the fault surface to meet the vein at a depth of 500 feet? (Use scale of 200 feet per inch.)

2. In a fold the slaty cleavage strikes N 75 W and dips 60° SW. The bedding on an overturned limb strikes N 20 W and dips 75° SW. What is the strike and plunge of the fold axis and the pitch of the fold axis as measured on the bedding?

3. On the foot-wall surface of a fault which strikes N 10 E and dips 25° SE the slickensides trend due east. Find the direction and plunge of the net slip and its pitch as measured on the fault surface.

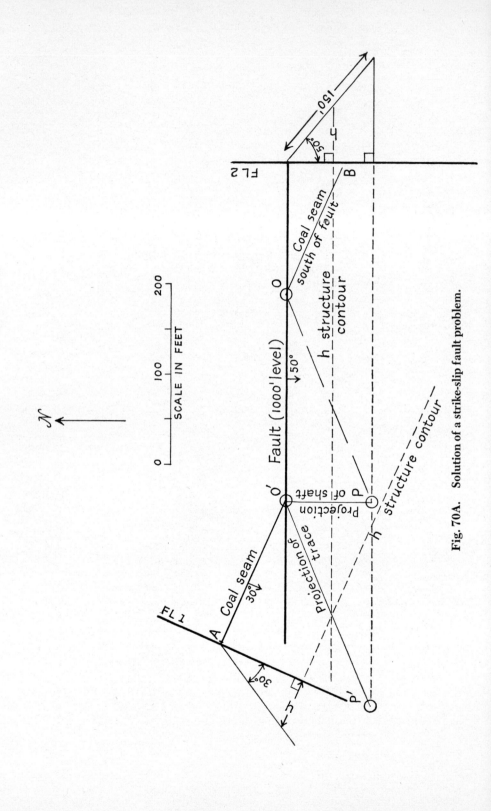

Fig. 70A.   Solution of a strike-slip fault problem.

CHAPTER 16

Solution of Fault Problems

THE QUANTITATIVE SOLUTION OF fault problems involves primarily the relative displacement of two initially adjacent points in the fault zone. The orthographic projection method is properly applicable only to motions that are translational along the fault zone or surface. If rotational movement is present, this method can be applied where translational motion can be approximated.

Translational motion may be essentially parallel to the dip of the fault (dip slip), parallel to the strike of the fault (strike slip), or at some intervening angle along the fault surface (oblique slip). Although geologically common, dip-slip and strike-slip faults are special cases of the oblique slip. Owing to their lack of vertical motion, strike-slip faults present much simpler problems compared to the others.

Strike-Slip Faults

Example: A coal seam whose strike and dip are N 65 W and 30° SW, respectively, is being followed southeastward along its strike at the 1000-foot level. The seam is cut off abruptly where it is crossed by an east-west strike-slip fault that dips 50° south. From this cut-off point a shaft which is sunk directly down the fault encounters the seam again at a distance of 150 feet. Where along the fault line would the vein be encountered again at the 1000-foot level?

Figure 70A is drawn for the 1000-foot level. The projection to this level of the trace of the seam on the fault is determined by means of two structure contours drawn for an arbitrary depth h. Point P is the projection to the map level of the point at which the seam is encountered by the 150-foot inclined shaft. It is found where the shaft intersects the fault contour corresponding to the inclined distance of 150 feet.

107

Before faulting, points P and P' were coincident. Therefore, point O' on the intersection of the trace with the fault line must have been displaced to the east in such a way that $O'O$ equals $P'P$. From O draw a line (OB) parallel to $O'A$. OB is thus the displaced vein at the 1000-foot level. The trace of the intersection of the seam and fault for the southern block must be PO.

Figure 70B is a block diagram of this situation showing analogous points and lines in three dimensions.

Dip-Slip Faults

Although dip-slip faults may be normal or reverse, the procedures developed here are applicable to either type. The variables involved in fault problems are generally (1) the dip and strike of the fault plane, (2) the dip and strike of the displaced structure, (3) the net slip, and (4) the strike separation (along the fault line). Most geologic problems resulting from faulting involve the determination of either the net slip or the strike separation if all the other information is known.

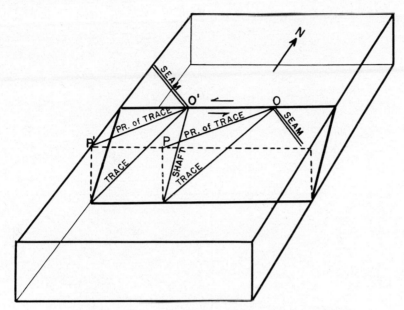

Fig. 70B.   Three-dimensional analysis of Figure 70A.

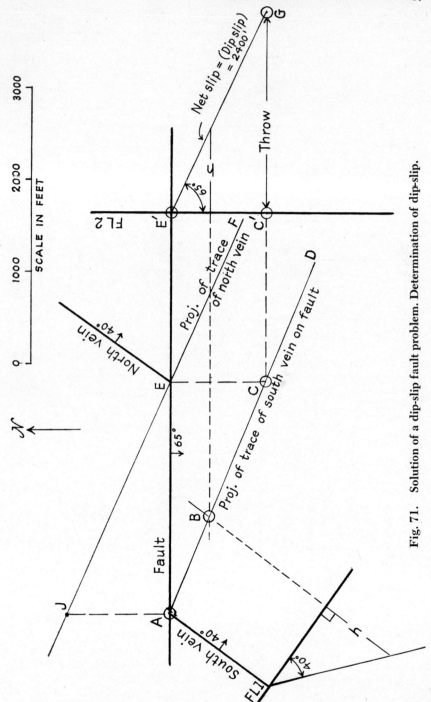

Fig. 71.   Solution of a dip-slip fault problem. Determination of dip-slip.

Example: An east-west dip-slip fault which dips 65° S causes a strike separation of 2500 feet for a vein that strikes N 35 E and dips 40° SE. Find the net slip, which in this case is the dip slip.

These relations are shown in Figure 71, which represents the plan view of a level surface, which may be considered as the surface of the earth or any desired mine level. Note that the north vein is displaced in the direction of dip (to the east), relative to the south vein. As this is a level surface, the north block must have moved up for such a displacement to occur. Thus, the fault is normal. To find the net slip, we must locate a point at depth on the south vein which was once adjacent to point E on the north vein.

Locate the horizontal projection of the trace of the south vein on the fault, using the procedure from Chapter 8. A is the location of this line at the surface and B at h depth. AD is the desired trace. A line parallel to AB from E is the horizontal projection of the trace of the north vein on the fault. Before faulting, line EF was in contact with line AD. As this is a dip-slip fault, motion was normal to the strike of the fault. Thus, if we draw a line normal to the fault through point E it will intersect line AD at C, the position of E before faulting. Clearly, EC is the horizontal component of the dip slip (heave). The true net slip (dip slip), which lies in the fault plane, can be found in a vertical section normal to the fault line, such as the section below FL2. E'G is the desired net slip (2400 feet). Incidentally, C'G is the throw. The three-dimensional relationships in this problem are shown in Figure 72. It should be noted that the problem could be solved in the same manner, working on the north, or up-dip, side of the fault. In this case AJ is the heave, and the net slip would be found by drawing the fault up-dip from FL2.

Example: Assume that in the above case another vein *(A)* which strikes N 15 W and dips 35° NE is found only on the south side of the fault. Locate its position to the north of the fault.

In the previous problem, the net slip was determined. This information can now be applied in the solution of the new problem. We can work on either the down- or up-dip side of the fault.

Refer to Figure 73A which shows the fault and vein A, whose continuation to the north of the fault is to be found. By means of structure contours the horizontal projection of the trace of the vein on the down-dip surface of the fault is located. The structure contour representing the appropriate throw for the net slip intersects the trace projection at point *P*. After faulting, a point originally in contact with *P* on the north block has been carried to point *Q*. Thus, a line from *Q* northward and parallel to vein A locates the displaced vein (*A₁*).

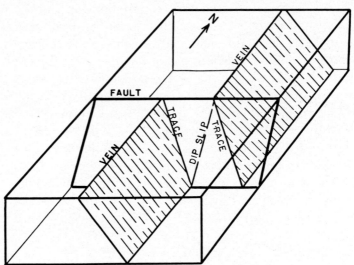

Fig. 72.   Three-dimensional analysis of Figure 71.

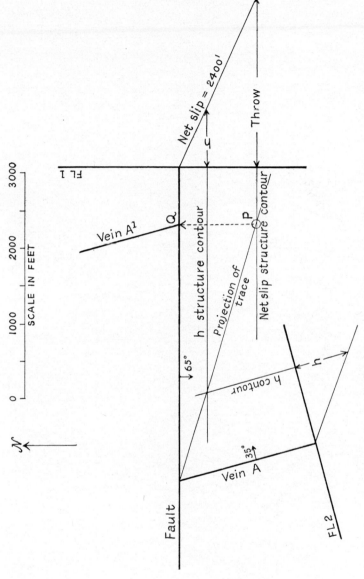

Fig. 73A. Solution of a dip-slip fault problem (hanging wall block). Determination of strike separation.

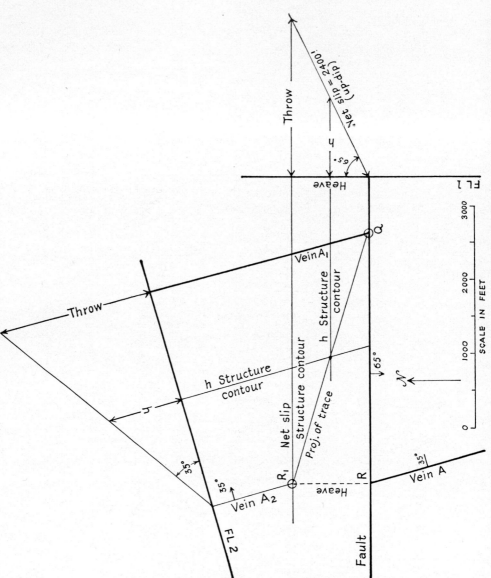

Fig. 73B. Solution of a dip-slip fault problem (footwall block). Determination of strike separation.

This problem can be solved just as readily by working on the north or up-dip side of the fault (Figure 73B). Point R is displaced northward to R_1 by a distance equal to the heave, so that vein A_2 represents the vein at the new position, vertically higher than vein A by the throw. If we draw the projection of the trace of the vein on the fault downward from point R_1, it will intersect the original fault line at Q, which marks the intersection of the vein to be found with the fault. Point Q can also be found by drawing a structure contour on vein A_2 for the throw depth (the original level of vein A). This structure contour intersects the fault at Q. Of course, this last is simply the determination of a unique point on the trace R_1Q.

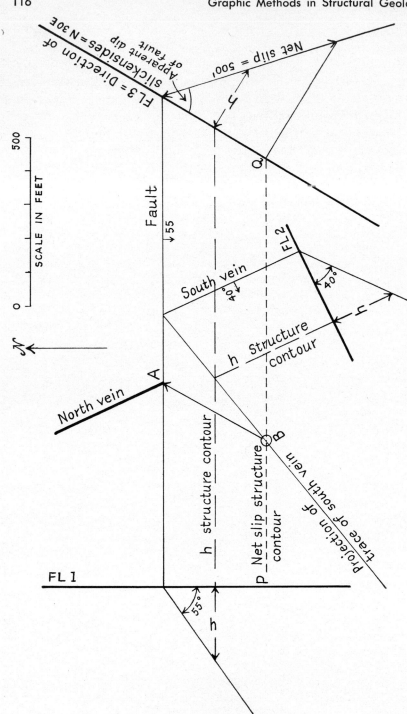

Fig. 74. Solution of an oblique-slip fault problem. Procedure 1.

Oblique-Slip Faults

These faults represent the general case in which the movement in the fault plane has both a strike-slip and a dip-slip component. The variables involved are the same as those for dip-slip faults.

Example: An east-west normal fault dips 55° S. The direction of slickensides on the fault surface is N 30 E, and the net slip is 500 feet. A vein which strikes N 25 W and dips 40° SW is found on the south side of the fault. Find the location of the vein north of the fault.

Its location is found here by using two variations of the orthographic projection procedure.

Construct the horizontal projection of the trace of the south vein and the fault, as shown in Figure 74. The true dip of the fault is shown in the section below $FL1$. From this, construct the apparent dip of the fault in the vertical plane which includes the slickensides as below $FL3$. Incidentally, this apparent dip is also the plunge of the slickensides. The true length of the net slip can be measured in this plane, and the structure contour (PQ) corresponding to the net slip depth can be drawn as shown. The intersection of this contour line and the projection of the trace gives a point (B) which, when moved back to the fault line parallel to the direction of the slickensides, locates the displaced north vein at A.

This problem can also be solved equally well by working on the north side of the fault, as was done for the dip-slip faults, above.

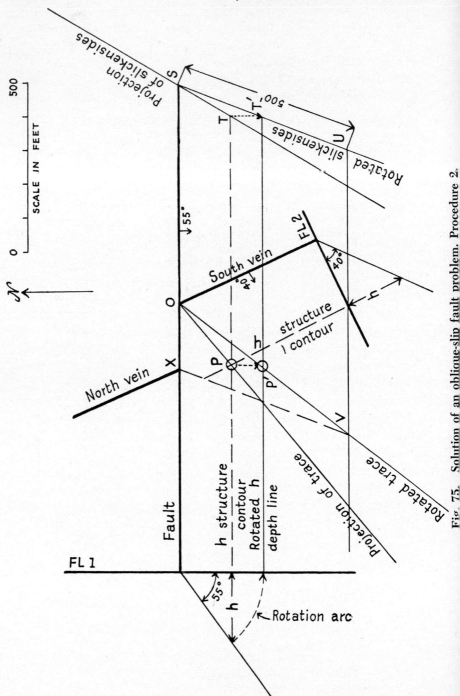

Fig. 75. Solution of an oblique-slip fault problem. Procedure 2.

Refer to Figure 75 for an alternate solution of the problem given above. Construct the horizontal projection of the trace of the south vein and the fault as in the previous solution (Figure 74), using the arbitrary vertical depth h. Then, rotate the fault plane into the horizontal. The depth line represented by the h structure contour will appear as shown, and the point P on the projection of the trace will be at P'. The actual trace of the north vein on the fault as shown on the rotated fault plane is thus the line from O through P'. (Incidentally, the acute angle between OP' and the fault line is the pitch of the trace measured in the plane of the fault.)

Let us now find the direction of the slickensides on the fault plane. Draw the horizontal projection of the slickensides, N 30 E. The projection of the slickensides at h depth is shown at point T, which on the rotated fault plane is at point T'. All motion along the fault plane is thus parallel to the line ST'. SU, which is 500 feet, represents the true net slip. A line through U parallel to the fault line is the locus of all points which were displaced the net-slip distance and direction at the time of faulting. This line cuts the trace at point V. After faulting, a point on the north block originally in contact with V was carried to point X which can be found by drawing a line from V to the fault line parallel to US. Point X thus locates the vein on the north block. *Note well that the previous problems on dip-slip faults could also be solved by following the above procedure of rotating the fault plane into the horizontal.*

Example: In this example the original and displaced positions of two veins, *A*, *A'* and *B*, *B'* of given strike and dip are shown on opposite sides of a fault of known strike and dip, in Figure 76. Find the direction and amount of net slip.

It is not necessary to know in advance whether the fault is dip slip or oblique slip when this kind of data is available, but the type of faulting does become obvious in the solution. By inspection of Figure 76, it is clear that the southeast block moved up, so that the fault must be normal.

Refer to Figure 77A. By means of structure contours on veins *A'* and *B'* and on the fault surface for the hanging wall, locate the projections of the traces of each of these veins on the fault surface. These are found as lines *A'C'* and *B'C'*. For simplicity, the constructions are not shown here, but the procedure is the same as that used in many earlier problems. Then draw *AC* and *BC* parallel to *A'C'* and *B'C'*, respectively. *AC* and *BC* are the projections of the traces of veins *A* and *B* on the fault surface of the foot wall.

Prior to faulting, the points of intersection of the two sets of traces (*C* and *C'*), must have been in contact. Thus, line *CC'* must be the projection of the net slip on the fault surface. The direction of *CC'* gives the bearing of the net slip. It becomes clear at this point that the fault had an oblique motion. The amount of net slip can be found in the vertical plane, which includes the net slip *CC'*, but first the true depths, represented by points *C* and *C'* must be found. *C* and *C'*, respectively, must lie on the two fault surface structure contours *CE* and *C'E'*, whose true depths are found in the vertical section below *FL*1, normal to the fault line. Thus, the depths *d* and *d'*, from the surface to the fault, correspond to the structure contours *CE* and *C'E'*, respectively, and hence to the depths of *C* and *C'*.

Below points *C* and *C'* in the vertical plane through these points, locate depths *d* and *d'*, respectively. For convenience in Figure 77A, this is done below *FL*2, which is parallel to *CC'*. The distance *PQ* in this plane is the required net slip and is scaled from the diagram.

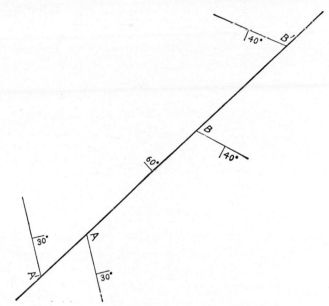

Fig. 76.   Map view of a fault and the displaced beds. Determination of net slip given in Figures 77A and B.

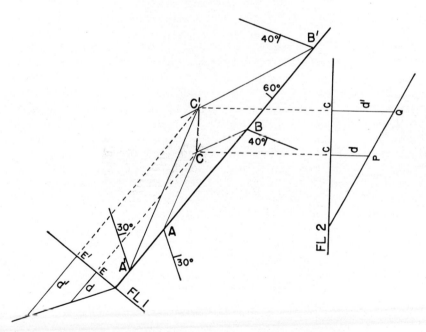

Fig. 77A.   Solution for the determination of net slip.

This quantity can also be found by rotating the fault plane into the horizontal and then measuring the required separation directly in this plane. Thus, in Figure 77B, when the fault is rotated to the horizontal, the point for which E is the projection is displaced to F, and similarly E' is displaced to F'. Hence, C at the surface would appear at G in the rotated fault plane (with the distance CG being equal and parallel to EF). C' would appear at G', with $C'G'$ being equal to $E'F'$. The distance GG' is the net slip. (If GG' is extended to meet the fault line, the included angle would be the pitch of the net slip measured on the fault plane.)

EXERCISES

1. A north-south strike-slip fault, whose west side is displaced 300 feet northward, dips 75° W and cuts a coal seam which strikes N 40 E and dips 40° NW. Designate the area wherein a vertical drill hole will intersect the coal seam at two different levels. (Note: this area will have three fixed boundaries, the fourth being indefinite.)

2. A vein which strikes N 28 W and dips 75° W is cut by an east-west normal dip-slip fault dipping 60° S and having a net slip of 200 feet. Assuming that you know the position of the vein to the south of the fault, find its position on the north side. (Note: you will find that this is a special case in which the trace of the vein on the fault is parallel to the net slip—a trace-slip fault.)

3. A north-south reverse dip-slip fault dips 35° W and cuts a vein that strikes N 60 W and dips 50° SW. If the strike separation of the vein along the fault is 400 feet, find the net slip, heave, and throw of the fault.

4. A normal dip-slip fault is oriented N 35 E, 65° SE. An east-west vein on the hanging wall is cut off by the fault. If the dip-slip is 350 feet, and the vein dips 45° N, locate the vein on the foot wall.

5. The slickensides on a fault which is oriented N 60 E, 60° NW, trend north-south. A vein oriented N 40 W, 35° SW shows a strike separation of 250 feet. Determine the net slip, strike slip, and dip slip. Solve for both a normal and a reverse fault.

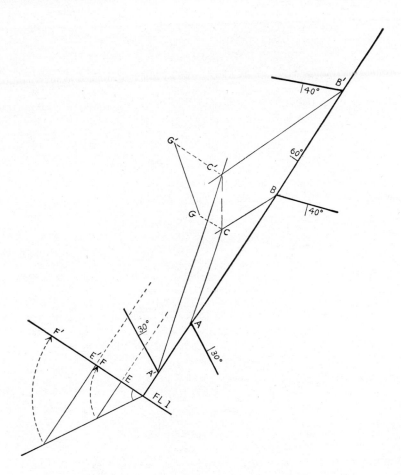

Fig. 77B.   Alternate solution for the determination of net slip.

PART III

Quantitative Graphic Procedures: Stereographic Projection

THE STEREOGRAPHIC PROJECTION has long been used in the study of crystallography for the graphic portrayal of symmetry elements of crystal systems and classes. It also can be used with great efficiency in the solution of three-dimensional problems in structural geology.

In our treatment of the stereographic procedure we will consider only its use in the solution of problems in structural geology. Its application in the plotting of joints, cleavage, and in petrofabrics simply involves one phase of the techniques developed in such solutions and will therefore not be given special consideration. As noted in the introduction to Part II, this projection can only be utilized for a complete solution when the problem is restricted to angular relationships—but this it can accomplish with remarkable ease. For those problems which also include factors of linear measure, such as the three-point problem, and fault displacements auxiliary orthographic procedures are necessary. Further, certain types of problems which cannot be solved by orthographic projection are easily soluble by stereographic procedures.

CHAPTER 17

Stereographic Projection and the Stereonet

STEREOGRAPHIC PROJECTION INVOLVES the projection of points from a spherical surface to a plane surface. It is usually convenient to start the projection lines from one point on the surface of a sphere and project only points from the opposite hemisphere. This is illustrated in Figure 78, where points shown on the hemisphere are projected by straight lines from Z to the underlying horizontal plane. Note that in this projection, the point O at the center of the sphere and the lowest point on the hemisphere directly below O, coincide at point O' in the projection (stereogram). The intersection of the dipping plane, AOBC, with the lower hemisphere gives the arc ABC, whose projection on the stereogram is the curve A'C'B'. The orientation of a line connecting A' and B' through O' gives the strike of the dipping plane. (Although this line is not a true element of the stereogram because it does not lie on the surface of the hemisphere, we will usually construct it to give greater clarity in the visualization of projections.) Any vertical plane passing through O will cut the hemisphere in a great circle, whose projection will be a straight line through O'. A horizontal plane passing through O, such as that of the upper surface of the hemisphere, meets the hemisphere in the great circle WNES, whose projection is the boundary circle W'N'E'S'. Any plane through O neither vertical nor horizontal, but dipping, similar to plane AOBC, will also cut the hemisphere in a great circle whose projection will resemble curve A'C'B'.

The main problem in the application of this procedure to structural geology will be to reduce structures consisting of planes and lines to corresponding lines and points on the surface of a hemisphere which can then be projected onto a two-dimensional surface.

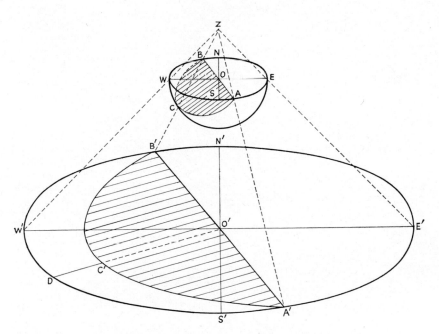

Fig. 78.   Diagram illustrating the principle of the stereographic projection.

In structural geology we deal with structures whose orientation in space is given by a compass direction and an angle of inclination. For this reason we use a hemisphere with co-ordinate markings similar to those of the earth, and turned so that the axis is horizontal. Furthermore, the plane of projection is always taken parallel to a meridian plane—a plane passing through the center of the sphere and both poles. In this way, the four cardinal compass points will lie in the horizontal (meridian) plane of the hemisphere. This is shown in Figure 79, which also shows the meridians of longitude and parallels of latitude on the undersurface of the hemisphere.

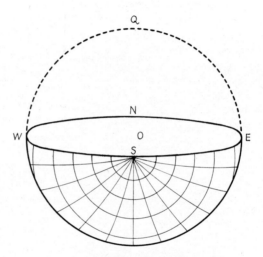

Fig. 79.   Diagram showing parallels and meridians drawn on the surface of
the lower hemisphere.

If we now imagine that meridians and parallels are drawn on the hemisphere for every two degrees, the stereographic projection of this hemisphere will appear as shown in Figure 80, which is called a *stereonet* or, more specifically, a *Wulff meridional stereonet*. This net provides the basic graph for the solution of structural geology problems similar to those given in Part II. The points (labeled 0 to 90) where the projected parallels intersect the circumference of the net gives compass bearings from the center of the net.

In Figure 80, the meridians of longitude can be considered as great circles formed where planes dipping at various angles and striking *NS* through *O* intersect the hemisphere. The straight line *NS* is the projection of a vertical plane striking north-south; and the lines of increasing curvature, westward or eastward, show projections of planes of decreasing dip, all striking north-south. The dip of a particular plane is measured inward from the circumference along the WE diameter. In the use of this stereonet, clearly, all vertical angles, regardless of dip direction, are most conveniently measured along either west-east or north-south diameters; usually the former is preferable. Interpolations can be made for angles of dip other than the multiples of two degrees for which the stereonet is drawn. This net, some tracing paper, a pencil, and a straightedge are the principal tools required.

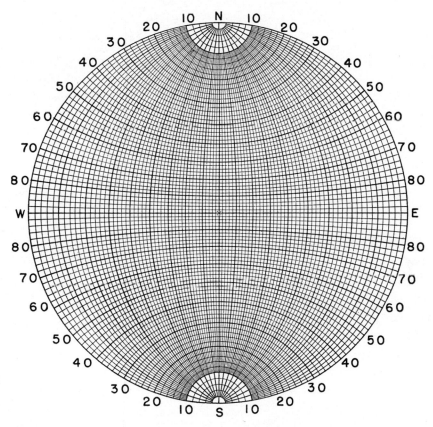

Fig. 80. The stereonet. (Removable stereonets for use with problems are included at the end of the book. These should be pasted to a cardboard backing.)

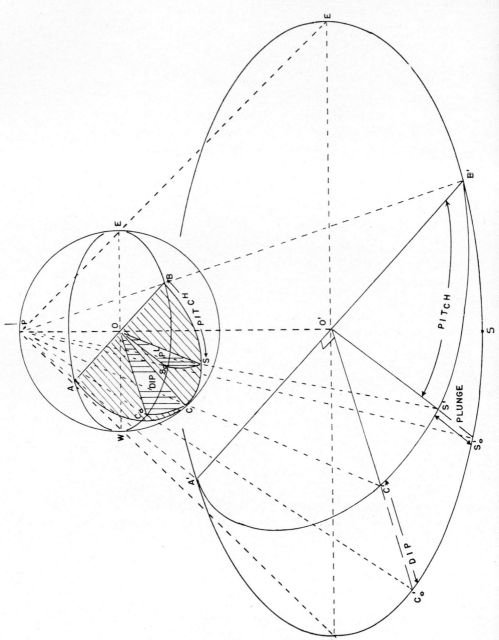

Fig. 91.   Perspective drawing showing the stereographic projection of a dipping bed.

Before considering specific problems it might be well to consider the application of this procedure to some common geologic parameters. Figure 81 shows in perspective the projection of a plane striking N 35 W and dipping 30° SW. Here, the arc C_0C, which measures the angle of dip, is the distance $C_0'C'$ on the projection. In the same way, the arc S_0S, which measures the plunge of an arbitrary line OS on the dipping plane, is shown by the distance $S_0'S'$ on the projection. This angle is also the apparent dip of the plane in the direction OS_0. Also, the arc BS is a measure of the pitch of line OS and is shown on the projection as arc $B'S'$.

CHAPTER 18

True and Apparent Dip

Apparent Dip from Strike and True Dip

From a known strike and dip, apparent dips in any desired direction can be obtained with great ease and a minimum of construction by means of the stereographic projection.

Example: A bed strikes N 35 W and dips 30° SW. Determine the apparent dips in vertical planes trending N 15 E, EW, NS, and N 60 W.

Place a piece of tracing paper over the stereonet and mark a reference point at the center.* Then draw a straight line (CD) through the center with the strike N 35 W; draw the dip direction from the center to the circumference of the net perpendicular to the strike line, as in Figure 82A. Because vertical angles must be measured on the stereonet along a diameter (preferably the east-west diameter), rotate the tracing paper by keeping the center points of tracing and stereonet coincident, until the strike line (CD) coincides with the north-south diameter and, hence, the dip direction with the west-east line. Then, as in Figure 82B, the distance AB is a measure of the true dip angle, just as in Figure 81 $C_0'C'$ is a measure of the angle having the arc C_0C. Draw the entire curve CBD following the curve on the stereonet for a plane dipping at 30 degrees. The projection of the dipping plane is now this curve.

To obtain apparent dips, rotate the tracing back to its original position, as in Figure 82C. Draw each of the apparent dip direc-

* In this and all following constructions, each stereogram shows both the tracing and the underlying stereonet drawn in abridged form. Note that with the exception of the dip angles on the west-east diameter of the net, all symbols within the net represent construction on the tracing paper. The short arrow on the tracing is used to locate true north. This is especially helpful when the stereogram (tracing) is rotated in the course of the solution.

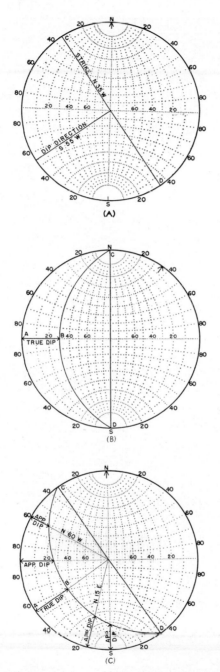

Fig. 82.   Solution for apparent dip from strike and true dip.

tions required. Note that the apparent dip angle in the N 15 E plane corresponds in orientation to the angle S_oOS, and the projection $S_o'S'$ in Figure 81. Apparent dips, being vertical angles, must also be measured along the west-east or north-south diameters. Thus, the apparent dip values in the WE and NS vertical planes can be read directly from the underlying stereonet (Figure 82C). To read the apparent dip angles for the N 15 E and the N 60 W planes, rotate the tracing until these directions coincide with the WE (or NS) lines. Any line from the center through curve CBD, except the true dip direction, is an apparent dip direction, and the corresponding apparent dip angle can be measured by rotating that direction to coincide with a diameter of the net.

True Dip from Strike and Apparent Dip

Example: A bed strikes N 40 E and has apparent dip of 30° N on a vertical cliff trending N 10 E. Find the true direction and angle of dip.

On tracing paper over the stereonet draw, as in Figure 83A, the strike and apparent dip directions. The direction of true dip must then be N 50 W as shown. In order to construct the apparent dip angle, turn the paper until the apparent dip direction matches a diameter, as in Figure 83B. Then measure off the 30 degrees as shown by AB. In order to find the true dip, rotate the tracing until the strike line coincides with the NS diameter of the net (Figure 83C). Point B lies on a meridian circle of the underlying stereonet. CBD, which is the tracing of this curve, is thus the projection of the dipping plane having the given strike and apparent dip. The true dip of this plane is measured along the WE diameter, as shown in Figure 83C and has a value of 48 degrees. Actually the true dip angle can be measured directly from the net without drawing CBD.

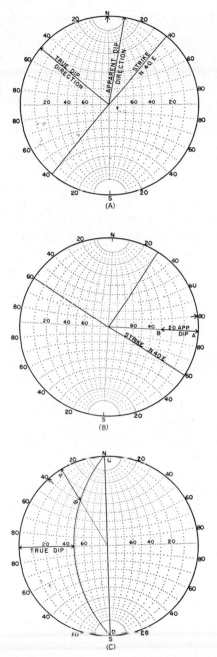

Fig. 83. Solution for true dip from strike and apparent dip.

True Dip from Two Apparent Dips

Although the following technique in connection with two apparent dips is directly applicable to surface data, it can also be used to solve the three-point problem by first reducing the linear depths to two apparent dips as explained earlier on p. 76.

Example: Consider the problem solved earlier on p. 72. The apparent dip of a bed is 26° NE on Cliff trending N 60 E. The same bed dips 19° SW on a cliff which trends N 10 E. Find the true direction and angle of dip.

In Figure 84A the two directions of apparent dip are drawn as shown. The apparent dips *AB* and *CD* are constructed by rotating the tracing so that each apparent dip direction lies in turn over the *WE* diameter along which the values 19 degrees and 26 degrees, respectively, are then measured. Rotate the tracing until points *B* and *C* lie on the same meridian circle (Figure 84B). From the foregoing examples, it is clear that this circle is the projection of the required dipping bed. The true angle of dip, measured in along the *WE* diameter, is 45 degrees. If the tracing is rotated back to its original orientation, as in Figure 84C, the strike, *EF*, is then measured as N 30 E, and the true dip direction is S 60 E.

EXERCISES

1. A coal seam strikes N 65 E and dips 35° NW. Find the apparent dip of the coal seam on cuts that trend N 10 E, N 20 W, and east-west.

2. A sequence of formations which strikes N 50 E shows an apparent dip of 35° N in a railroad cut. What is the true dip?

3. In an area of regional dip, two apparent dips are determined on a shale bed: 15° E and 21° S 20 E. Find the true angle and direction of dip.

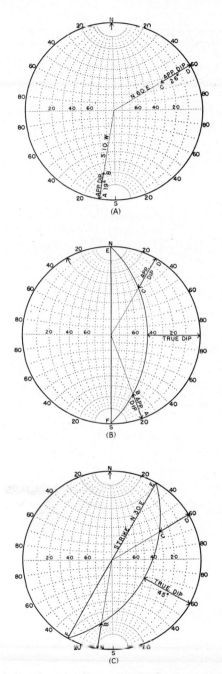

Fig. 84.   Solution for true dip and strike from two apparent dips.

CHAPTER 19

Strike and Dip from Vertical Drill-Core Data

Example: Consider a problem similar to that solved earlier in Chapter 12, p. 84. Two vertical drill holes, which start from a level surface, lie 2500 feet apart on a NE-SW line. The southwest hole reaches a given bed at the depth of 800 feet, and the other at a depth of 2000 feet. The bedding makes an angle of 40 degrees with the axis of the hole (core-bedding angle). Find the strike and dip of the bed(s).

The dip is obviously 50 degrees, the complement of the core-bedding angle. On an auxiliary diagram determine the apparent dip of the bed in the vertical plane (*NE-SW*) which includes the drill holes. This construction is done on the lower part of Figure 57, but for this problem A_1B_1 trends *SW-NE* instead of *EW*. The problem is now reduced to the solution for the strike and dip direction when the true dip (without direction) and an apparent dip angle and direction are known.

Lay off the direction *OQ* and the angle *PQ* of the apparent dip (taken from the auxiliary diagram), as in Figure 85. Then rotate the tracing until point *P* lies on a meridian circle corresponding to a true dip of 50 degrees. Two such positions are possible, namely, the circles corresponding to the true dip planes *APB* and *CPD*. Thus, *AB* and *CD* are the possible strike directions having bearings *NB* and *ND*, respectively. The unique strike cannot be obtained without further data.

The determination of strike and dip from inclined core holes requires a different treatment and is reserved for the chapters which involve the rotation of the sphere of projection.

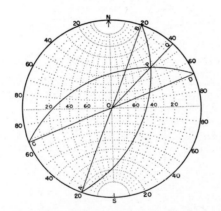

Fig. 85.   Solution for strike and dip from vertical drill-core data.

CHAPTER 20

Intersecting Surfaces; Plunge and Pitch;
Lineation

**Example: On p. 103 the following example was solved: a vein strik-
ing N 40 E and dipping 60° SE intersects a bed which strikes N 50 W
and dips 40° SW. Find the position in space of the line of intersection
as given by (1) its surface projection, (2) its angle of plunge, and (3) its
angle of pitch on both vein and bed.**

The other required parts of the solution on page 104 cannot
be obtained directly by this procedure. But after the spacial relations are obtained here, the parts of the problem involving linear
construction can be solved easily by separate geometric diagrams
similar to those used in Chapter 15.

Draw on the tracing the projections of the vein and bed as shown
in Figure 86 by curves AEB and CED, respectively. OE is the surface projection of the line of intersection of these planes. The
plunge of this line is given by the distance EF, which can be evaluated by turning it to a diameter of the net. This is analogous to the
arc S_0S and its projection $S_0'S'$ in Figure 81. Note also in Figure 81
that the pitch of the line OS on the dipping bed is measured by the
arc BS and its projection $B'S'$. In Figure 86, DE by analogy is the
pitch of the line of intersection as measured on the bed, and AE
is the pitch as measured on the vein. To determine the numerical
value of the pitch ED, line the strike of the bed along the north-
south diameter. Then along the underlying meridian circle measure the number of degrees from D to E; in the same way AE can
be evaluated.

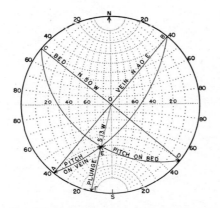

Fig. 86.   Solution for the case of intersecting surfaces; determination of
plunge and pitch of the line of intersection.

Example: Find the position in space of a lineation of given pitch measured on a plane of given dip and strike.

On tracing paper placed over the stereonet draw the projection of an arbitrary inclined plane *ACB* (Figure 87). With *AB* rotated into the north-south position, lay off an arbitrary pitch angle *AD* along the appropriate meridian circle. With the tracing rotated to its original position, the bearing of *OD* is the position in space of the lineation, and *DE* is the measure of the plunge.

Example: Find the acute angle of intersection between two arbitrarily chosen, intersecting joint sets.

OG is the line of intersection of the two joint planes *ABC* and *DEF* shown in Figure 88. *GH* is the plunge of this line. It should be realized that the angle between two intersecting planes must be measured in a plane that is normal to both of the planes and hence their line of intersection. The strike of such a plane must thus be perpendicular to this line of intersection and its dip must be opposite in direction and be the complement of the plunge of this line. To locate such a plane, draw *JK* perpendicular to *OG* and mark point *L*, 90 degrees away from *G*. Then draw the plane *JLK* by tracing the appropriate meridian circle after first placing *JK* on the north-south line. *S* and *T* are points of intersection of this new plane with the two joint planes. Therefore the arc distance *ST* is the measure of the acute angle between the joint planes.

EXERCISES

1. An ore body occurs along the plunging trough formed where a basic dike crosses a limestone layer. The limestone strikes N 20 E and dips 20° W, but the dike strikes N 15 W and dips 65° W. Find the orientation and plunge of the ore body and its pitch on both the vein and bed.

2. A fault surface strikes N 70 W and dips at 55° NE. The slickensides on this surface have a pitch of 35° E. Find the bearing and plunge of the slickensides.

3. Find the acute angle of intersection between the limestone bed and dike described in Problem 1, above.

4. Planar structures are visible on three oblique sections of a granite mass. If the orientation of these sections and the pitch of the planar

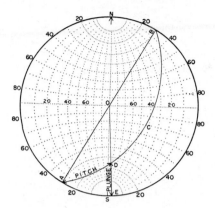

Fig. 87. Finding the position in space of a given lineation.

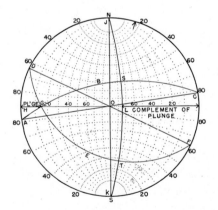

Fig. 88. Solution for the acute angle of intersection between two intersecting joint sets.

structure on each is as given below, find the true orientation of the planar structure.

Section	Pitch of Planar Structure
A. N 30 E 30° east	40° N
B. N 74 E 70° south	54° E
C. N 12 W 50° west	52° S

CHAPTER 21

Nonrotational Faults

THIS SECTION DEALS WITH problems involving faults where the motion in the fault plane is essentially linear, as opposed to faults of the pivotal or hinge type where motion is rotational. In general, the stereographic procedure is a useful but limited auxiliary tool for the solution of fault problems of the nonrotational type. Where applicable, the solution is simplified considerably. For example, oblique slip-fault problems are as easily solved as those for dip-slip faults, which was certainly not the case with the orthographic procedures.

Example: Figure 89A shows a map of a dipping vein displaced by a fault. The direction of the fault movement, shown by slickensides, is toward the northwest, as indicated. Find the position in space and the amount of net slip.

On tracing paper over the stereonet draw the projections of the fault plane and the bed (*FPF'* and *APA'*, respectively, in Figure 89B), disregarding the separation of the displaced parts of the bed. *OS* is the trend of the net slip (or slickensides). *NS'* is its bearing; *S'S* is its plunge; and *FS* is the measure of the pitch of the net slip on the fault surface. *OP* is the projection of the trace of the bed on the fault, and arc *F'P* is the pitch of this trace on the fault plane. The simple graphic construction in Figure 89C gives the amount of net slip. Consider the fault plane as rotated to the horizontal about the fault line. *MN* is then the horizontal separation, to scale, of the displaced bed, taken from Figure 89A. The pitch of both the trace and net slip on the fault plane can be constructed from the values obtained from Figure 89B. The amount of the net slip, *NP*, is scaled off as shown.

Note that if this were a dip-slip fault, the net-slip direction of slickensides (*OS* in Figure 89B) would be perpendicular to *FF'*,

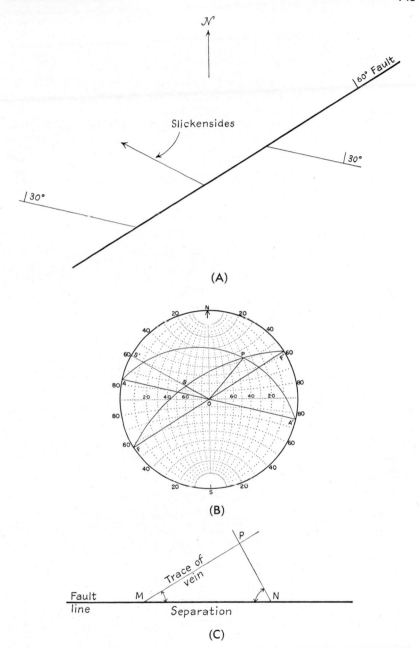

Fig. 89. Statement (A), and solution (B and C), of nonrotational oblique-slip fault problem. Angle PMN (89C) is the pitch of the trace of the vein on the fault (angle F'P of Figure 89B); angle PNM is the pitch of the net slip on the fault (Angle FS of Figure 89B). (After Bucher)

and *PN* in Figure 89C would be perpendicular to *MN*. The procedure for the solution, however, would be identical with that just described.

Example: Consider the problem solved earlier on p. 120, where the displacement of two veins are given, but the direction as well as the amount of net slip is not known. The problem is set up in Figure 90A where two veins, *A* and *B*, are displaced by a fault having the strike and dip shown. Find both the position in space and the amount of net slip.

Transfer the map data to the stereogram as shown in figure 90B, drawing all strikes through the center point. The projections of the fault plane and veins *A* and *B* are shown as planes *FPF'*, *APA'*, and *BQB'*, respectively. The projection of the trace of vein *A* on the fault is *OP*, which has a pitch *FP* (22°) in the fault plane. The projection of the trace of vein *B* on the fault is *OQ*, which has a pitch *FQ* (28°).

As linear distances are again involved, we must use auxiliary diagrams. In Figure 90C, these trace projections are transferred to the map, so that *A'C* and *B'C* are the trace projections for the hanging-wall fault surface, and *AC'* and *BC'* are the trace projections for the foot-wall fault surface. Thus, *C'* is the projection of the point of intersection of the two veins on the foot-wall fault surface, and *C* is the similar point for the hanging wall. As the two points *C* and *C'* were originally in contact, *CC'* must be the projection of the net slip. To determine its position in space, lay off the direction of *CC'* as *OE'* on the stereogram in Figure 90B. *NE'* is thus the bearing of the net slip, and *E'E* is its plunge.

The numerical value of the net slip is determined from a second auxiliary diagram, Figure 90D, which is drawn on the fault surface rotated into the horizontal about the fault line. The lines *AC'*, *BC'* and *A'C*, *B'C* are drawn from their original map positions (Figure 90A) to points *C'* and *C* by means of the pitch angles, determined from Figure 90B. The length of line *CC'* when scaled off the diagram gives the net slip.

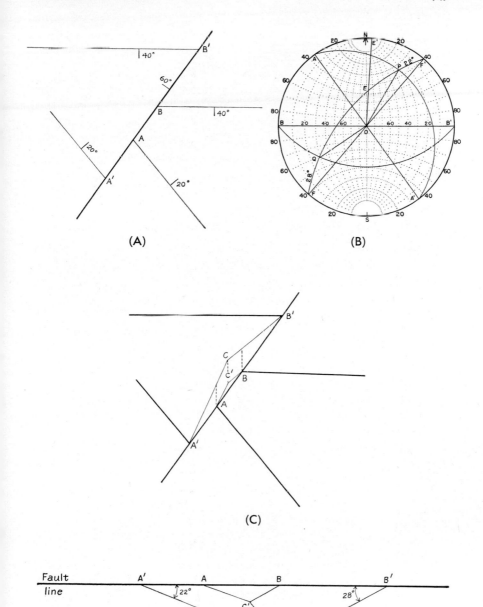

Fig. 90.   Variation of nonrotational, oblique-slip fault problem.
(After Bucher)

Example: A normal fault displaces a vein located at Q along the fault line, as shown in Figure 91A. The strikes and dips are as shown. If the slickensides trend north-south, and the net slip is known to be 500 feet, find the position of the vein north of the fault.

The projections of the fault and vein on the stereogram are shown as FPF' and APA' in Figure 91B. OP is the projection of the trace of the vein on the fault. $P'P$ is the plunge of the trace and FP is its pitch ($50°$) on the fault surface. The trend of the slickensides is OMN. Their pitch is $F'M$ ($76°$), as measured on the fault plane.

In the auxiliary diagram (Figure 91C), the fault plane is rotated into the horizontal about the fault line. Draw the slickensides on the fault surface, using the pitch as determined from Figure 91B. Measure off the net slip RS (500 feet) along the direction of slip (slickensides) from point R. From S draw SQ, the trace of the vein on the fault, so that the angle SQR is equal to 50 degrees, or the pitch of this trace on the fault surface. Lay off the distance QR on Figure 91A, thus locating the position of the vein north of the fault.

EXERCISES

1. A reverse dip-slip fault that strikes N 15 E and dips $35°$ W cuts a vein that strikes N 60 W and dips $50°$ SW. If the strike separation along the fault line is 400 feet, find the net slip, heave, and throw of the fault.

2. The slickensides on a fault which is oriented N 60 E, $60°$ NW trend north-south. A vein oriented N 40 W, $35°$ SW shows a strike separation of 250 feet. Determine the net slip, strike slip, and dip slip. Solve for both a normal and reverse fault.

3. An east-west fault has cut two veins. Vein A, which strikes N 45 W and dips $30°$ NE, appears on the southern block 500 feet to the east of its displaced portion on the northern block. Vein B, which strikes N 50 E and dips $45°$ NW, is found on the northern block at a distance of 240 feet to the east of vein A on the same block. On the southern block vein B is 200 feet west of its displaced northern part. Find the amount, plunge, and pitch of the net slip, and the amount of dip slip and strike slip.

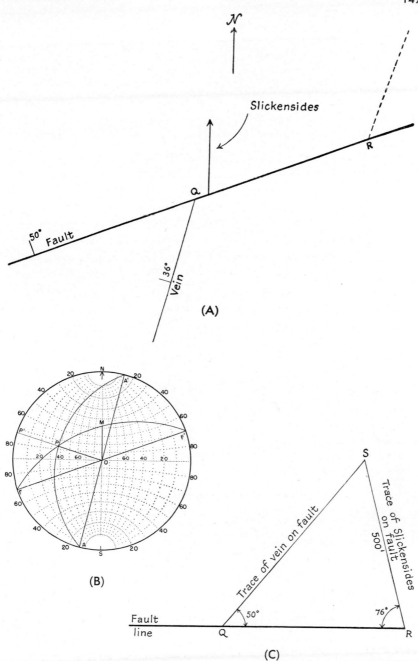

Fig. 91.   Solution for displaced vein when net slip is known in the case of a
nonrotational, oblique-slip fault.

CHAPTER 22

Problems Involving Rotation of the Sphere of Projection About a Horizontal Axis

IN THIS CHAPTER WE will deal with a type of problem whose solution requires the rotation of structures into positions in space different from those existing now. This may, for example, involve the restoration of a structure to its position before deformation. Such solutions require rotation of the fundamental sphere of projection about either a horizontal or an inclined axis. We will consider first problems involving rotation of the sphere about a horizontal axis and, in the following chapter, rotation about inclined axes.

Unconformities and "Two Tilt" Problems

Example: Figure 92A shows a geologic map of two sets of dipping beds (*A* and *B*), separated by an angular unconformity. Strikes and dips are designated in the diagram; the angular unconformity is, of course, parallel to the overlying beds (sequence *B*). Find the original strike and dip of sequence *A* prior to the tilting of sequence *B*.

Construct the projections of sequences *A* and *B* on the tracing over the stereonet as shown by *APA'* and *BQB'*, respectively, in Figure 92B.

To determine the orientation of plane *APA'* when sequence *B* is rotated to the horizontal, we must imagine that the entire hemisphere of projection is rotated about the horizontal axis *BOB'* until sequence *B* (*BQB'*) reaches the horizontal. Remember that the perimeter of the net is the projection of a horizontal plane. Thus, on rotation of *BQB'* about *BOB'*, *Q* is displaced to *Q'* and *BQ'B'* represents the horizontal orientation of sequence *B*.

To find the location of any point on the stereogram after rotation, it is convenient to turn the tracing until the axis of rotation

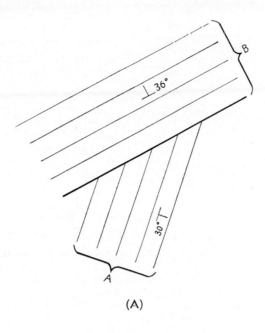

(A)

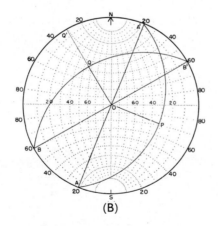

(B)

Fig. 92A, B. Solution of the "two-tilt" problem involving an angular unconformity.

(in this case BOB') coincides with the north-south diameter of the net. Then the new points will be found by moving through the required rotation angle along appropriate west-east parallels.

Figure 92C shows the tracing turned so that *BOB'* coincides with the north-south diameter of the net. Upon rotating the sphere about *BOB'*, *Q* is rotated 36 degrees to the horizontal at *Q'*. At the same time, the arbitrary points *D*, *E*, and *P* on plane *APA'* are also rotated 36° W along the appropriate curves to points *D' E'* and *P'*.

Now the tracing is turned, as in Figure 92D, until points *D'*, *E'*, and *P'* all lie on the same meridian circle, thus giving the new position for sequence *A* of $A_1P'A_1'$. The angle *RR'* is thus the original angle of dip of sequence *A* prior to the tilting of the overlying sequence *B*. This is part of the required solution. To find the new strike direction, the tracing must be turned to its original orientation, as in Figure 92B, so that the north point of the tracing coincides with north point of the underlying net. The original strike of sequence *A* will then be NA_1' degrees to the east of north, with the dip to the southeast.

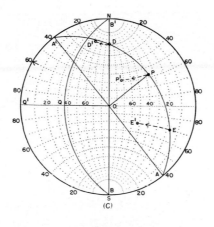

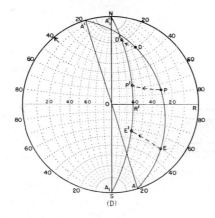

Fig. 92C, D.   Solution of the "two-tilt" problem involving an angular unconformity.

Use of Poles of Planes

The stereographic construction necessary for the solution of problems involving many planes can be greatly simplified by the use of points representing *poles* of planes, in place of the projections of entire planes. Remember that a plane is projected as a curved line on the stereogram, because such a line is really the projection of the great circle formed by the intersection of a dipping plane with the hemisphere of projection. Imagine a line perpendicular to a dipping plane and passing through the center of the hemisphere of projection, as shown in Figure 93A. Line OQ normal to plane APB intersects the hemisphere at point Q. Thus, angle QOP and its arc QP must be 90 degrees, and point Q is designated the pole of the plane APB. Clearly, every plane with a given orientation has a unique pole, and every pole on the hemisphere is uniquely associated with a given plane. Note that the projection of the pole is always a point, as Q'. Therefore, we can work with the one-dimensional pole-point projection, always remembering that it represents a two-dimensional plane. In the projection (Figure 93B) Q' defines the plane $A'P'B'$, and points P' and Q' are separated by 90 degrees. Note, therefore, that the plunge of a pole is always the complement of the dip of its plane.

Example: Let us solve the previous problem, using poles instead of planes, and note the greater simplicity in construction.

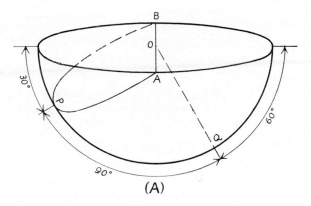

(A)

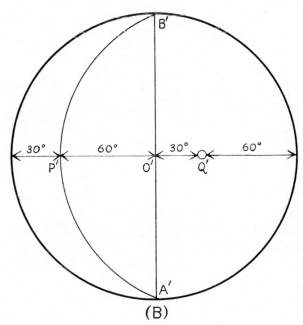

(B)

Fig. 93.   Diagrams illustrating the principle of "poles" of planes.

In Figure 94A, points A and B are the poles of the planes APA' and BQB' of Figure 92B. The plunge of each pole is shown.

In order to rotate sequence B into the horizontal (as was done in Figure 92C), pole B must be moved to coincide with the vertical, at O. Following the earlier procedure, turn the tracing so that B lies on the west-east diameter, Figure 94B. Then rotate the hemisphere about the north-south diameter so that B moves to the vertical at O, causing A to be displaced through the same angle, and along the appropriate parallel, to A'.

In Figure 94C the stereogram tracing is shown turned back to its original orientation, with the original locations of poles A and B also marked. Although it is not necessary for the solution, the plane for sequence A ($A_1R'A_1'$ of Figure 92D) is also shown. A' is the pole of this plane. The dip measured as RR' could have been measured just as readily as OA'. The strike is the bearing NA_1', which, of course, could be measured without drawing the plane itself. Clearly, the construction procedures here as well as in all previous cases have been much elaborated for the sake of clarity.

Incidentally, the most common graphical method of depicting the orientation of joints is to plot their poles on a stereonet. The use of points instead of planes greatly facilitates the study of the distribution of the joint planes in a region. Any preferred orientations are shown by a clustering of the points.

Lineation

It may be necessary to find the orientation of linear features prior to deformation, as is involved in some studies of lineation, traces of planes, paleomagnetism, and the like. The latter offers a very interesting subject for the application of the stereographic method to the study of a linear feature. For example, magnetite grains might become magnetized during deposition and, following lithification, would preserve the direction of the earth's magnetic field at this time. Magnetic studies of rocks of different ages therefore permit the determination of the direction of the earth's magnetic field at various times in earth history. If, however, the rock is deformed from its position at the time of the acquired magnetism, it must be restored to this original position before the true paleomagnetic field can be determined.

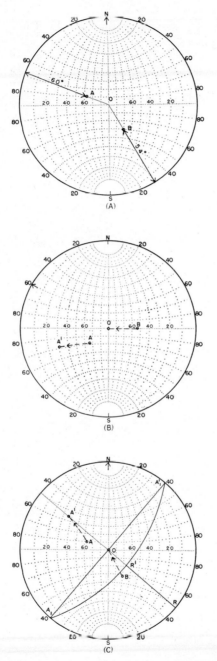

Fig. 94.   Solution of the two-tilt problem of Figure 92, using poles.

Example: The vector of the earth's magnetic field as determined from magnetized particles in a sediment is now found to plunge 30° N 10 W. The enclosing sediment is on the west flank of an anticline having a horizontal axis; the beds strike N 50 W and dip 45° SW. Find the paleomagnetic vector at the time of deposition.

The sediment must be unfolded to its (horizontal) position at the time of deposition in order to determine the original direction of the magnetic field. In Figure 95A, APA′ is the projection of the dipping sediment, and AOA′ is both the strike direction of the sediment and the fold axis. Point Q is the projection of the vector of the earth's paleomagnetic field. The plunge is RQ.

In order to rotate the sediment (APA′) to the horizontal, turn the tracing until the fold axis AOA′ is coincident with the north-south diameter, as in Figure 95B. Then rotate the hemisphere about AOA′ so that point P moves 45 degrees to the horizontal position at P′. Point Q will move the same number of degrees and in the same direction along the appropriate parallel to Q′. Then turn the tracing back to its original orientation (Figure 95C). The bearing NT is the magnetic declination at the time of deposition, and TQ′ is the inclination of the field vector.

To solve this problem using poles, locate the pole of the dipping sedimentary plane at P, and the magnetic field vector at Q (Figure 95D). Turn the tracing so that P lies on the west-east diameter, with Q moving as shown in Figure 95E. In unfolding the sediment into the horizontal, the pole P moves to the vertical and coincides with O, while Q moves through the same angle to Q′. In Figure 95F the tracing is turned to the original orientation, with Q′ appearing in the position shown. NR is the declination, and Q′R is the inclination, of the magnetic field vector.

EXERCISES

1. A series of beds below an angular unconformity strike N 80 W and dip 60° SW. The beds overlying and parallel to the unconformity strike N 30 E and dip 35° SE. Find the dip of the lower set of beds prior to the second deformation.

2. The vector of the earth's past magnetic field is found to plunge 40°, N 20 E in sediments which strike N 30 W and dip 35° SW. What was the paleomagnetic field orientation at the time of deposition?

3. A vertical fault which strikes N 10 W pivots the southern portion of the east block downward through an angle of 25 degrees. What is the new strike and dip of the beds on the east block after faulting, if their strike and dip on the undisturbed west block is N 30 E, 40° SE?

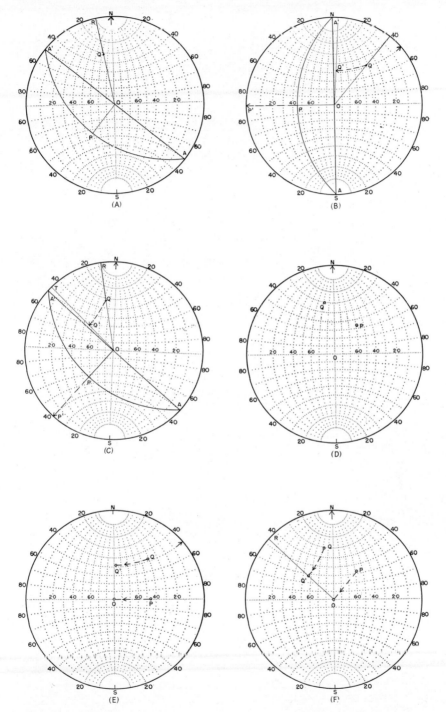

Fig. 95.   Example of solution for paleomagnetic field vector using poles.

CHAPTER 23

Problems Involving Rotation of the Sphere of Projection About an Inclined Axis

To APPLY STEREOGRAPHIC PROCEDURES to problems which involve an inclined axis of rotation, we simply perform the auxiliary step of rotating the sphere so that the inclined axis becomes horizontal. Then we perform the desired rotation of the sphere about this horizontal axis, as in the preceding chapter. In the last step we reverse the initial rotation, returning the axis to its original inclined position. For simplicity in construction we will use the scheme of projecting poles of planes rather than the planes themselves.

Rotational Faults

Example: A rotational fault that strikes N 10 E and dips 60° E has cut a series of horizontal beds. The east (hanging wall) block is pivoted downward through an angle of 20 degrees about an axis through point X, as in Figure 96A. Find the strike and dip of the beds on the downthrown block.

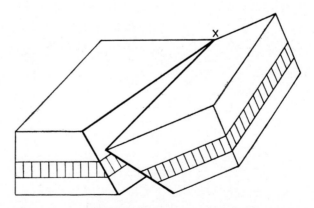

Fig. 96A.   Rotational fault which cuts horizontal beds.

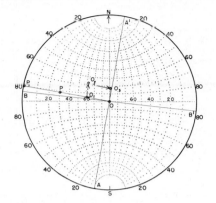

Fig. 96B.   Solution of a rotational fault problem for horizontal beds.

The axis of rotation, through X, must clearly be normal to the fault plane, or plunge 30°, N 80 W. The projection of this axis is shown as point P in Figure 96B. Since the axis of rotation is a line normal to the fault plane, point P is also the pole of the inclined fault plane. As the beds on the undisturbed foot wall are horizontal, their pole must be on a vertical whose projection coincides with point O. The results from each step of the solution are shown on the single diagram of Figure 96B, so that the individual steps must be imagined or can be performed separately by the reader.

To bring the inclined axis of fault rotation into the horizontal, and, incidentally, the fault plane into the vertical, the sphere is rotated about the horizontal axis AA', which is normal to OP. P is thus carried to P_1, and O (the pole of the initially horizontal beds) the same number of degrees to O_1. (These movements, of course, are carried out along the west-east diameter of the stereonet, after the tracing is temporarily turned so that AA' coincides with the north-south diameter.)

We now rotate the sphere through an angle of 20 degrees about the horizontal fault axis OP_1 and observe the new position of the pole of the sedimentary beds (O). Remember that all rotations of the sphere must be carried out about the north-south diameter of the stereonet, so that the motions of points on the stereogram can follow the appropriate parallels. Therefore, turn the tracing so that OP_1 coincides with ON and then move O_1 through 20 degrees (the fault pivot angle) to O_2.

After finding the position of O_2, we must reverse the initial 30-degree rotation of the inclined fault axis. This reverse rotation about AA' brings O_2 to O_3 (and P_1 back to P). O_3 is the pole of the beds on the downthrown hanging wall. The angular distance from O to O_3 is the dip (18° S) of the beds, and the line BB' normal to OO_3 gives the orientation of the strike, whose bearing is N 84 W, as shown. If desired, the projection of the plane of the dipping beds could be drawn using the earlier procedures.

Example: Consider a problem similar to the previous one except that the beds are tilted instead of horizontal. A pivotal fault which strikes N 70 W and dips 50° NE cuts a series of beds which strikes N 15 W and dips 35° SW. If the eastern side of the hanging wall pivots downward through an angle of 40 degrees about an axis at the northern edge of the region, find the orientation of the beds after faulting.

The pole of the fault plane (or the axis of fault rotation) is located at point A in Figure 97, and that for the unfaulted dipping beds is at point B. To bring the axis of fault rotation into the horizontal, the sphere is rotated so that A moves to A_1 and B thus moves through the same angle (40 degrees) to B_1. Now, with OA_1 as the axis of rotation (fault axis), B_1 moves to B_2, through the required rotation of 40 degrees. When the initial rotation of the fault axis into the horizontal is reversed in the last step, B_2 is carried to B_3, which is the pole of the beds after displacement. The dip angle is OB_3, with the direction of dip being to the south, and the strike is a line normal to OB_3. (Note that the necessary turnings of the tracing paper to bring the axes of rotation into coincidence with the north-south diameter of the stereonet are no longer mentioned.)

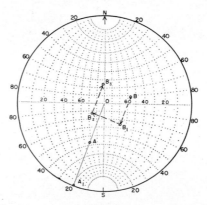

Fig. 97.   Solution of a rotational fault problem for tilted beds.

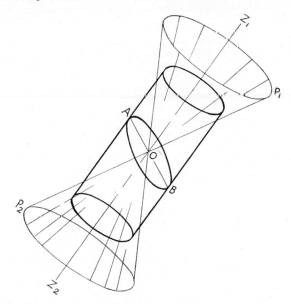

Fig. 98.   Illustration of the factors involved in an inclined core-hole problem.

Inclined Drill Holes

The stereographic procedure can also be used in the solution of problems involving unoriented cores from inclined drill holes in which no marker horizons are encountered. In Part II, the treatment of such cases was made easier by considering one vertical and one inclined drill hole. However, the stereographic procedure permits equally easy treatment of two inclined drill holes. Before solving such a problem let us first analyze the geometry involved.

Figure 98 illustrates a portion of an inclined core on which the trace of an oblique bedding plane is shown as the ellipse, centered at point O. The line P_1OP_2 is the normal to this bedding plane, and points P_1 and P_2 can be considered as opposite poles of the plane. Z_1OZ_2 is the axis of the core. The bedding makes an angle with this core axis, Z_1OA, the core-bedding angle (and the equal vertical angle Z_2OB). Since angle AOP_1 is a right angle, Z_1OP_1 must be the complement of angle Z_1OA (and Z_2OP_2 is the complement of Z_2OB).

When a core is drawn, the orientation of the axis (Z_1OZ_2) is known, but the true orientation of the bedding is lost because of the rotation of the drill stem. Thus, the normal, OP_1, might be anywhere on the surface of the upper cone (Figure 98), and OP_2 might lie anywhere on the surface of the lower cone. The cones are formed by revolving the normal to the bedding about the core axis. Because the lower cone is symmetrical with the upper and the normals are continuous from one cone to the other, one cone simply repeats the information given by the other.

If a second core, inclined at a different angle, is available and the core-bedding angle can be determined, a similar construction gives a second double cone. Since this method of solution is used when no marker horizon and only core-bedding angles are available, the cores can be treated as though they intersect. The resulting double cones from each core can be considered as having a common vertex. The two double cones must intersect and can have from one to four common lines of intersection, each line representing a possible orientation of the normal to the bedding plane. These normals can then be translated directly into possible strikes and dips of particular bedding planes.

It will be recalled from Part II that the number of possibilities is a function of the core-bedding angles and the mutual inclinations of the core holes. If no conical intersections occur, either the bedding is not uniform between the two holes or the data are inaccurate.

Example: A core from hole A, which plunges S 30 W at 65 degrees, shows a core-bedding angle of 70 degrees. No marker horizon is encountered. A second core from a nearby hole B, which plunges N 80 E at 45 degrees shows a core-bedding angle of 30 degrees. Find the possible orientation(s) of the bedding.

Points A and B of Figure 99A are the projections of the two holes in proper orientation.

In Figure 98 again, assume the vertex, O, to be at the center of the sphere of projection. Then each cone will cut the surface of the sphere in a circle centered on the core axis. Each point on each circle corresponds to a possible position of a normal to the bedding, and each circle is thus the locus of all possible poles to the bedding.

If we imagine the axes of both cores intersecting at the center of the sphere of projection, their associated double cones will form two pairs of intersecting circles on the sphere of projection. Consequently, our main problem is to locate these circles, centered at A and B, respectively (Figure 99A), and note the points of intersection, which, in turn, are the poles of possible bedding planes. To draw the appropriate circles, use is made of the small circles about N and S on the stereonet. But first the axes of the holes (or the cones) must be rotated into the horizontal, so that they, in turn, can be made to coincide with the north-south diameter of the net.

The two holes must lie in a common plane, which is found by turning the tracing until points A and B lie on the same meridian circle (the projection of this common plane), as in Figure 99B. This operation simplifies the procedure of getting the two core axes into the horizontal, which is now done (Figure 99B) by rotating the sphere so that points A and B follow the appropriate small circles to positions A_1 and B_1, respectively.

It must now be re-emphasized that we deal with the lower hemisphere only in our projection procedure. Hence, when the sphere is rotated so that a double cone is in the horizontal, the upper half of each cone is omitted, as shown in Figure 99C. However, diametrically opposite portions of each complete cone repeat each other. Thus, the missing upper portion of cone A has its counterpart in the lower section of cone A'. If we consider the lower sections of both members of the double cone or the corresponding semicircular traces, no data are lost in the projection of these traces. In Figure 99B, points A_1' and B_1' are the projections in the horizontal plane of the opposite ends of the conical axes shown at A_1 and B_1.

The results of the next two steps are shown in Figure 99D. Turn the tracing so that the double-cone axis A_1A_1' lies on the north-south diameter. To construct the traces on the hemisphere of the double cone about A_1A_1', draw the semicircular projections by following the small circles of 20-degree radius. This is the angle between the normal to the bedding and the core axis for hole A, or the complement of the core-bedding angle. Then turn the tracing so that axis B_1B_1' coincides with the north-south diameter, as in Figure 99D, and draw the appropriate semicircular projections, following the small circles of 60-degree radius. The four semicircles intersect at the points P and Q, which are the poles, therefore, of possible bedding positions. To find their true orientations, we must restore the drill cores to their original orientations by reversing all of the previous operations.

The operations of Figure 99E reverse those of Figure 99B. In this process P and Q move to P_1 and Q_1 along the appropriate small circles. Note that these points move along either the same or diametrically opposite small circles during this reverse rotation.

Finally, the tracing is returned to the original orientation of Figure 99A, with P_1 and Q_1 moving to the positions shown in Figure 99F. P_1 and Q_1 here are the poles of the possible true positions of the beds, whose actual strikes and dips can easily be found, as in previous solutions. In actual practice the stages shown can be reduced to the use of one or at most two graphical diagrams.

In problems of this type, the circles of projection, such as those in Figure 99D, can intersect in from one to four points, depending on core-bedding angles and the plunge relations of the core axes. Refer again to Figure 99D. Clearly, if the angle between the normal to the bedding and the core axis increased, the circles about A_1 and A_1' would increase in radius. At a particular value, each of these circles would intersect one circle about B_1 and B_1' and be tangent to the other circle at diametrically opposite but identical points. This would give three pole positions. If the circles about A_1 and A_1' were increased further in radius, each would intersect both circles about B_1 and B_1' and thus give four intersections or pole positions. Further, if the circles about A_1, A_1', B_1 and B_1' were reduced appropriately, they would become tangent at diametrically opposite but identical points, giving a unique pole position and, thus, a unique strike and dip.

EXERCISES

1. A rotational fault that strikes N 15 W and dips 50° W cuts a series of horizontal beds. The southern end of the west block is pivoted downward through an angle of 30 degrees. Find the orientation of the beds on the downthrown block.

2. On the northeast side of a fault, a series of beds strike N 25 E and dip 35° NW, and a vein which strikes N 30 E dips 50° SE. On the southwest side of the fault, the beds strike N 70 W and dip 36° SW, whereas the vein strikes N 60 E and dips 30° NW. If the fault strikes N 50 W and dips 30° NE, find the amount and direction of rotation.

3. A pivotal fault which strikes N 60 E and dips 40° NW cuts a series of beds which strikes N 20 E and dips 40° SE. If the western side of the hanging wall pivots downward through 30 degrees about an axis at the northern edge of the region, find the orientation of the beds on the downthrown block.

4. Hole A plunges N 35 E at 60 degrees and shows a core-bedding angle of 70 degrees. Hole B plunges S 75 W at 50 degrees and shows a core-bedding angle of 35 degrees. If no marker beds are found, what are the possible orientations of the bedding?

5. A symmetrical anticline whose beds dip at 45 degrees plunges 20° N 35 E. The past magnetic field is determined to plunge 50° N 10 W from measurements made on the west flank of the fold. What was the true magnetic field vector at the time of deposition?

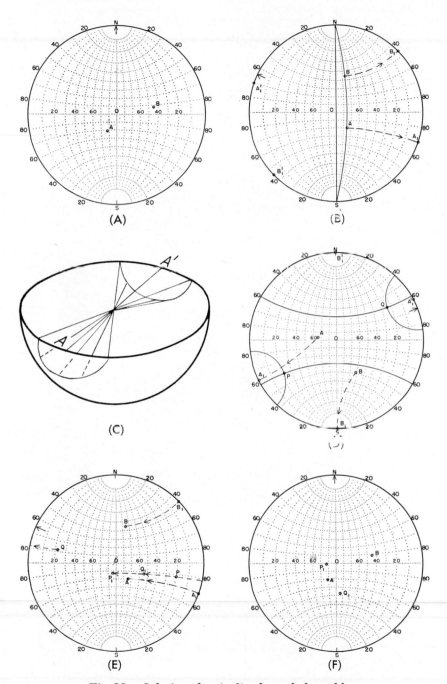

Fig. 99.   Solution of an inclined core-hole problem.

APPENDIX A

Construction of an Ellipse

IN MANY OF THE PROBLEMS given in the text it is necessary to construct an ellipse with a fair degree of accuracy. A convenient method of construction for the type of problems encountered is given below.

Let us consider the construction of an ellipse for a case similar to that illustrated in Figure 60, which involves an inclined drill hole. In Figure 100A, AD is the inclined drill hole, and AB and AC are elements of the resulting inclined cone, which represents possible positions of the inclined bed. Such a cone intersects the ground surface in an ellipse which we desire to construct.

BC is the major axis of the ellipse, and BE the semimajor axis. Thus E is the center of the ellipse. In order to determine the length of the minor axis, which is necessary in the construction used, extend AD as shown by the broken line. Through E, draw the line GEF perpendicular to the extended line AD. Draw an arc with radius FG about F. Line EH, perpendicular to GEF, is the semiminor axis.

On a strip of paper lay off the semimajor axis (xb), and the semiminor axis (xa), as shown in Figure 100B. Then draw the major and minor axes as shown in Figure 100C. Place the strip of paper so that point b is on the minor axis and point a is on the major axis; point x will then lie on the ellipse. By moving the strip of paper while keeping point b on the minor axis and point a on the major axis, point x will be found the trace the required ellipse.

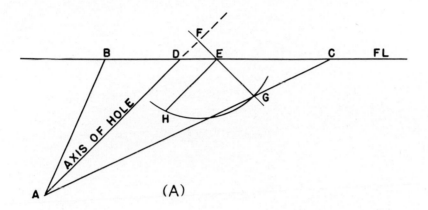

(A)

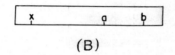

(B)

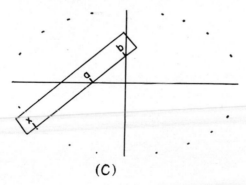

(C)

Fig. 100.   Method of constructing an ellipse.

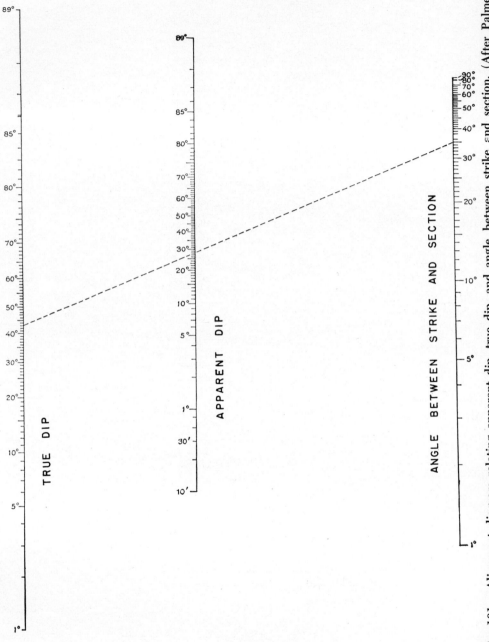

Fig. 101. Alignment diagram relating apparent dip, true dip, and angle between strike and section. (After Palmer)

APPENDIX B

Alignment Diagrams

SOME OF THE TYPES of problems solved earlier by projection methods can also be solved quickly and easily without construction by means of graphs known as alignment diagrams. In its simplest form, an alignment diagram consists of three parallel scales of variable quantities. These scales are calibrated so that when cut by a straight line determined by two known values the unknown quantity can be read directly off the third scale. This procedure lends itself readily to the solution of problems involving true and apparent dip, depth to an horizon, thickness and width of outcrop of a bed.

Figure 101 is an alignment diagram giving the relationship among the variables of true dip, apparent dip, and the angle between the strike of the beds and the section. Any one of these can be determined if the other two are known. Thus, since the straight line shown connects a true dip of 43°, an apparent dip of 28°, and an angle between strike and section of 35°, any one of these values can be determined if the other two are known.

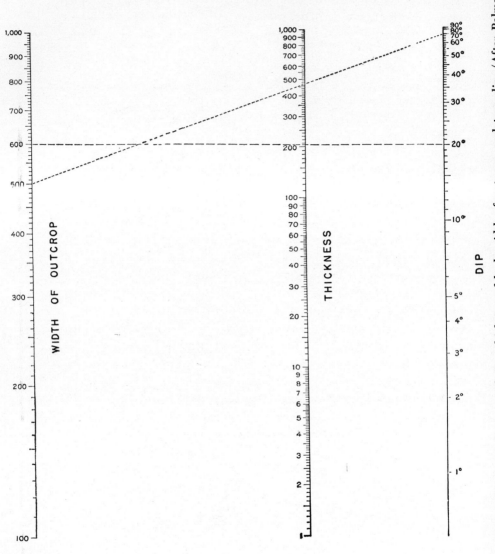

Fig. 102.   Alignment diagram relating thickness of bed, width of outcrop, and true dip. (After Palmer)

Figure 102 shows the relationship among the variables of width of outcrop, thickness of beds, and the angle of dip. Note that the width of outcrop here is measured on a level surface perpendicular to the strike. Again, any one of these three variables can be determined if the other two are known. Thus, from the straight line shown a thickness of 206 feet is indicated for a horizonal width of outcrop of 600 feet and a dip of 20°.

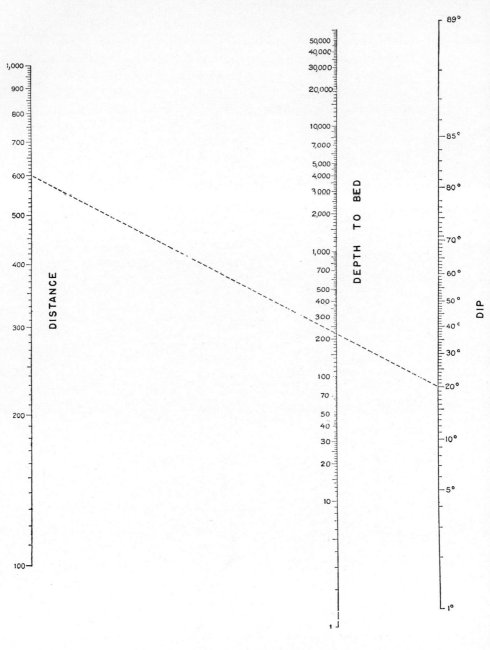

Fig. 103.   Alignment diagram relating true dip and depth to a bed at a given distance from the outcrop. (After Palmer)

Figure 103 shows the relationship among the following: angle of dip of a bed, the depth from a flat surface to the bed from a point, and a given perpendicular distance from the surface outcrop to the point. Thus, if a bed dips at 20°, then at a point 600 feet in a direction down dip from the surface outcrop the depth to the bed is 220 feet.

Somewhat more complicated alignment diagrams can be used to solve problems involving more than three variables, such as those in which the ground is sloping or distances are measured oblique to the strike. In such cases a graphical construction of the kind described in Chapters 10 and 13 is usually found to be readily applicable. However, such additional alignment diagrams are given in sources quoted in the bibliography.

APPENDIX C

Selected Bibliography

BECKWITH, R. H., "Fault Problems in Fault Planes," *Geol. Soc. America Bull.*, Vol. 58 (January, 1947), pp. 79–108.

BILLINGS, M. P., *Structural Geology*, 2nd ed. (Englewood Cliffs, N.J., Prentice-Hall, 1954), 514 pp.

BOUCHER, F. G., HILDEBRANDT, A. B., and HAGEN, H. B., "New Dip Logging Method," *Am. Assoc. Petroleum Geologists Bull.*, Vol. 34 (October, 1950), pp. 2007–2026.

BUCHER, W. H., "The Stereographic Projection, a Handy Tool for the Practical Geologist," *Jour. Geology*, Vol. 52 (May, 1944), pp. 191–212.

CLARK, R. H., and McINTYRE, D. B., "The Use of the Terms Pitch and Plunge," *Am. Jour. Sci.*, Vol. 249 (August, 1951), pp. 591–599.

COTTON, L. A., and GARRETTY, M. D., "Use of the Stereographic Projection in Solving Problems in Structural and Mining Geology," *Geological Bull.* No. 2 (1945), North Broken Hill Ltd. (Roneoed.).

DAKE, C. L., and BROWN, J. S., *Interpretation of Topographic and Geologic Maps*, (New York, McGraw-Hill, 1925), 355 pp.

FISHER, D. J., "Problems of Two Tilts and the Stereographic Projection," *Am. Assoc. Petroleum Geologists Bull.*, Vol. 22 (September, 1938), pp. 1261–1271.

——, "A New Projection Protractor," *Jour. Geology*, Vol. 49 (April–May, 1941), pp. 292–323 (May–June, 1949), pp. 419–442.

HOBSON, G. D., "A Graphical Solution of the Problem of Two Tilts," *Proc. Geol. Assoc.*, Vol. 54 (March, 1943), pp. 29–32.

HUBBERT, M. K., "Graphic Solution of Strike and Dip from Two Angular Components," *Am. Assoc. Petroleum Geologists Bull.*, Vol. 15 (March, 1931), pp. 283–286.

INGERSON, E., "Apparatus for Direct Measurement of Linear Structures," *Amer. Mineralogist*, Vol. 27 (September, 1942), pp. 721–725.

JOHNSON, C. H., "New Mathematical and 'Stereographic Net' Solutions to the Problem of Two Tilts—With Applications to Core Orientation," *Am. Assoc. Petroleum Geologists Bull.*, Vol. 23 (May, 1939), pp. 663–685.

JOHNSTON, W. D., JR., and NOLAN, T. B., "Isometric Block Diagrams in Mining Geology," *Econ. Geol.*, Vol. 32 (August, 1937), pp. 550–569.

LEVENS, A. S., *Nomography* (New York, Wiley, 1948), 176 pp.

LOBECK, A. K., *Block Diagrams* (New York, Wiley, 1924), 206 pp.

MEAD, W. J., "Determination of Attitude of Concealed Bedded Formations by Diamond Drilling," *Econ. Geol.*, Vol. 21 (January, 1921), pp. 37–47.

MERTIE, J. B., JR., "Graphic and Mechanical Computation of Thickness of Strata and Distance to a Stratum," *U. S. Geological Survey Prof. Paper*, No. 129, (1922), pp. 39–52.

NEVIN, C. M., *Principles of Structural Geology*, 4th ed. (New York, Wiley, 1949), 410 pp.

PALMER, H. S., "New Graphic Method for Determining the Depth and Thickness of Strata and the Projection of Dip," *U. S. Geological Survey Prof. Paper*, No. 120 (1918), pp. 123–128.

PHILLIPS, F. C., *The Use of Stereographic Projection in Structural Geology* (London, Edward Arnold Ltd., 1954), 86 pp.

PLATT, J. I., and CHALLINOR, J., *Simple Geological Structures* (London, Thomas Murby, 1954), 56 pp.

WALLACE, R. E., "A Stereographic Calculator," *Jour. Geology*, Vol. 56 (September, 1948), pp. 488–490.

———, "Determination of Dip and Strike by Indirect Observations in the Field and from Aerial Photographs," *Jour. Geology*, Vol. 58 (May, 1950), pp. 269–280.

WILLIS, B., and WILLIS, R., *Geologic Structures*, 3rd. ed. (New York, McGraw-Hill, 1934), 544 pp.

INDEX

Age relations, 13
Alignment diagrams, 170–175
Angular unconformity, 55, 150–151, 153
Apparent dip
  definition, 68
  from alignment diagram, 170–171
  relationship to true dip, 68–73, 132–137
Apishapa quadrangle, 19
Axes of rotation
  horizontal, 150–159
  inclined, 160–167
Axial trace, 25
Axis of fold
  horizontal, 24–25, 30
  plunging, 28–31

Batholith, 58
Bedded rocks, 1
Block diagrams, 2–3
Bucher, W. H., 145–147

Clarion quadrangle, 9
Cleveland quadrangle, 49
Contacts, intrusive, 58
Core-bedding angle, 85, 165

Dayton quadrangle, 21
Depth of strata
  by alignment diagram, 174–175
  by orthographic projection, 94–99
Dike, 58
Dip
  apparent, 68–73, 132–137, 170–171
  true, 12–13, 68–69
Disconformity, 54–55
Drill-hole problems
  inclined, 88–93, 163–167
  vertical, 84–88

Ellipse, construction of, 168–169

Fairfield quadrangle, 51

Faults
  dip-slip, 108–115
  nonrotational, 144–149
  oblique-slip, 116–123, 144–149
  rotational, 44–47, 160–162
  strike, 36–39, 48–51
  strike-slip, 106–108
  transverse, 40–43, 52–53
Folds
  asymmetric, 26–27, 67
  description of, 24–29
  outcrop patterns of, 30–35
  plunging, 28–29, 67
  symmetric, 26
Fold line, 60–63

Gadsden quadrangle, 33
Geologic illustration, 2
Geologic maps
  Apishapa quadrangle, 19
  Central Pennsylvania, 34
  Clarion quadrangle, 9
  Cleveland quadrangle, 49
  Dayton quadrangle, 21
  description, 4
  Fairfield quadrangle, 51
  faulted strata, 48–53
  folded strata, 32–35
  Gadsden quadrangle, 33
  Gettysburg quadrangle, 53
  horizontal strata, 9
  Three Forks quadrangle, 57
  tilted strata, 18–21
Geologic sections
  construction of, 10–11, 22–23
  description, 4–5
Gettysburg quadrangle, 53

Hade, 85
Heave, 111
Horizontal structure, 6–11
  outcrop pattern, 6–9

Intersecting surfaces, 102, 140
Intrusive contacts, 58
Isometric projection, 60

Laccolith, 58
Lineation, 102, 140–143, 156–159

Mead, W. J., 91, 93
Migration of outcrop, 16–17

Net slip, 108, 111, 120–121
Nonconformity, 54–55
Normal projection, 60

Offset
    simple, 40–41
    with gap, 42–43
    with overlap, 42–43, 52–53
Omission of beds, 36–41
Orthographic projection,
    elements of, 59–63
Outcrop patterns
    completion of, 100–101
    faulted strata, 36–53
    folded strata, 30–35
    horizontal strata, 6–9
    tilted strata, 18–21
    variation with thickness and dip, 15,
      95
Overlap, 42–43, 52–53

Palmer, H. S., 170, 172, 174
Pitch
    calculation of, 102–105, 140–143
    definition, 28–29
Plane of projection, 60
Plunge
    calculation of, 102–105, 140–143
    definition, 28–29
Poles of planes, 154–157
Profile, construction of, 10–11
Projection
    orthographic, 59–63
    stereographic, 59, 125–131
Projection line, 60

Repetition of beds, 36–41
Rotational faults, 44–47, 160–162
Rule of V's, 17

Sill, 58
Sphere of projection
    definition of, 126
    rotation of, 150
Stereonet, 126–131
Stock, 58
Strike, 12–13, 68–69
Strike faults, 36–39, 48–51
Structure contours, 64–67
Structure sections
    construction of, 10–11, 22–23
    description, 4–5

Thickness of strata
    by alignment diagram, 172–173
    by orthographic projection, 94–99
Three Forks quadrangle, 57
Three-point problems, 74–83
    apparent dip method, 74–77
    geometric methods, 80–83
    projection method, 78–80
    two points at same elevation, 74–75
Throw, 111
Tilted structure
    age relations, 13
    migration of outcrop, 16–17
    width of outcrop, 14–15
    outcrop patterns of, 18–21
Trace, 102
Transverse faults, 40–43, 52–53
True dip, 12–13, 68–69
Two-tilt problem, 150–153

Unconformities, 54–55, 150–151, 153
    angular unconformity, 55, 150–151,
      153
    disconformity, 54–55
    nonconformity, 54–55

V's, Rule of, 17

Width of outcrop, 14–15, 172–173
Wulff meridional net, 128

Zig-zag ridges, 30–31

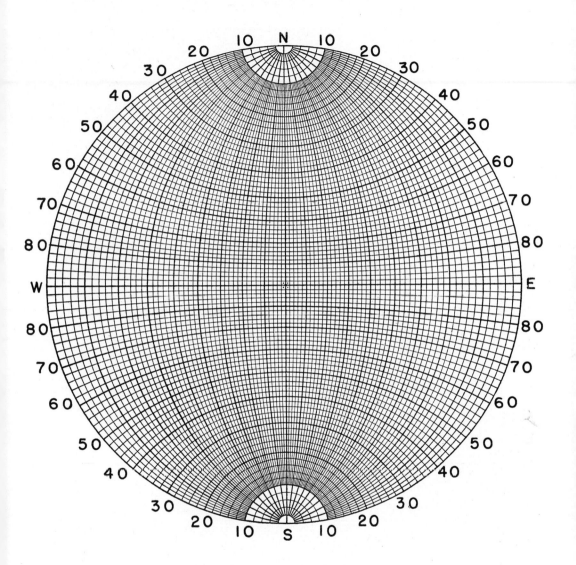